This book is dedicated to Perrin, who always inspires.
All things then become possible.

DEADLY HARVEST

THE END OF MANKIND

TEXT AND ILLUSTRATIONS BY
THOMAS C. RAMEY

Design by Lloyd Greenberg Design, LLC

ISBN: 978-0-9850545-3-3

Note: The majority of endnotes have been converted
from their original present tense to past tense
to serve the book's theme.

Pen and ink portrait drawings on pages 36, 52, 63,
and 98 are based on photographs by Steve McCurry.

Insects in pen and ink drawings on pages 14, 18, 100,
114, and 123 were inspired by photographs
by David M. Phillips.

Charles Square Press

www.thedeadlyharvest.com

TO SAVE THE WORLD
REQUIRES FAITH AND COURAGE:
FAITH IN REASON, AND COURAGE
TO PROCLAIM WHAT REASON
SHOWS TO BE TRUE.

— BERTRAND RUSSELL —

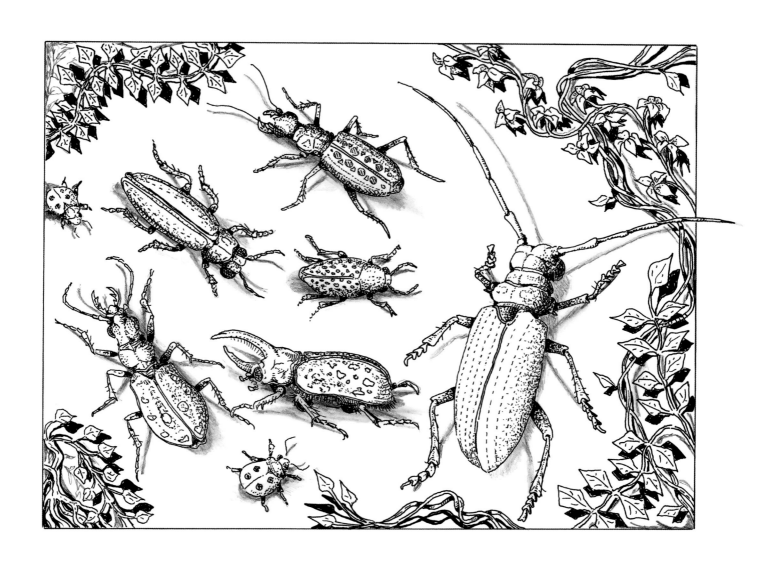

PREFACE

HOW IS IT THAT ONE SPECIES, MAN, IS HAVING SUCH A MONUMENTAL IMPACT on the other tens of millions of species on earth? How is it that this one species is changing the make-up of the planet to the degree that we are exceeding planetary survival margins? The "why" is complex, and a challenge to explain. The "how," though, is clear from every scientific vantage point. This book attempts to get at both the "how" and the "why." There is no aspect of life on earth that has not been impacted.

The book begins with a look at insects, as they represent, and have for millions of years, the largest number of species on earth, numbering 30 million. That they have survived and thrived for as long as they have puts in perspective how Man, as a sole species, has impacted the planet in just the last 300 years.

In addition to looking at manmade climate change, damage to the environment and biodiversity, the book examines the social destabilization fomented by fewer resources for an ever increasing population, failed states and conflict, migrating humanity, and mankind's seemingly endless need to exert supremacy of one group's beliefs over another.

We have known for decades about the changes humans are fostering and their impact, either immediate or potential. The perplexing question, as we move closer to irreversible damage, is how is it possible that we are knowingly doing this to ourselves? Among other things, this book is my attempt to answer that question, with the hope that the most farsighted among us will work toward solutions.

SPECIES: A SET OF ANIMALS OR PLANTS, MEMBERS OF WHICH HAVE SIMILAR CHARACTERISTICS TO EACH OTHER AND WHICH CAN BREED WITH EACH OTHER.

— CAMBRIDGE DICTIONARY —

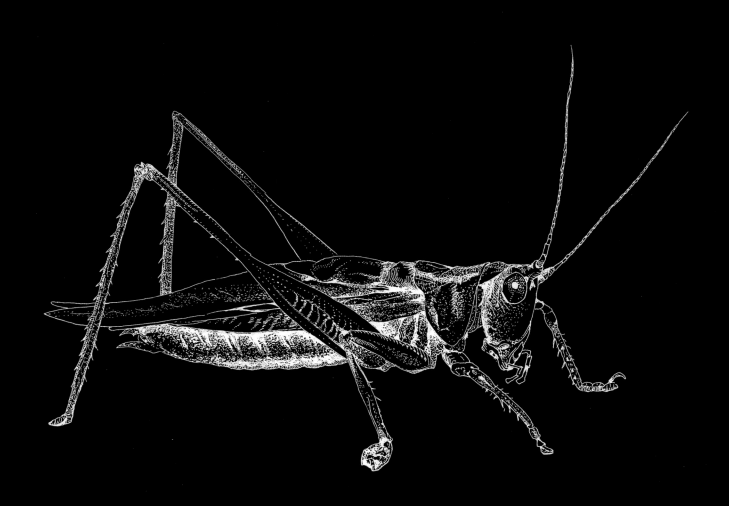

TABLE OF CONTENTS

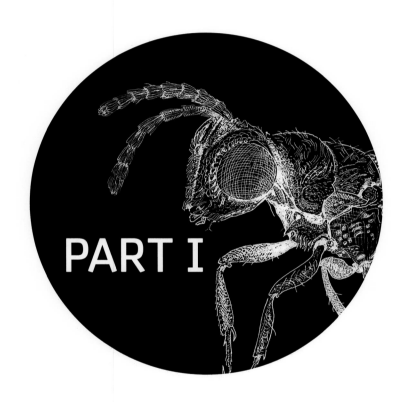

PART I

CHAPTER 1:

400 Million Years

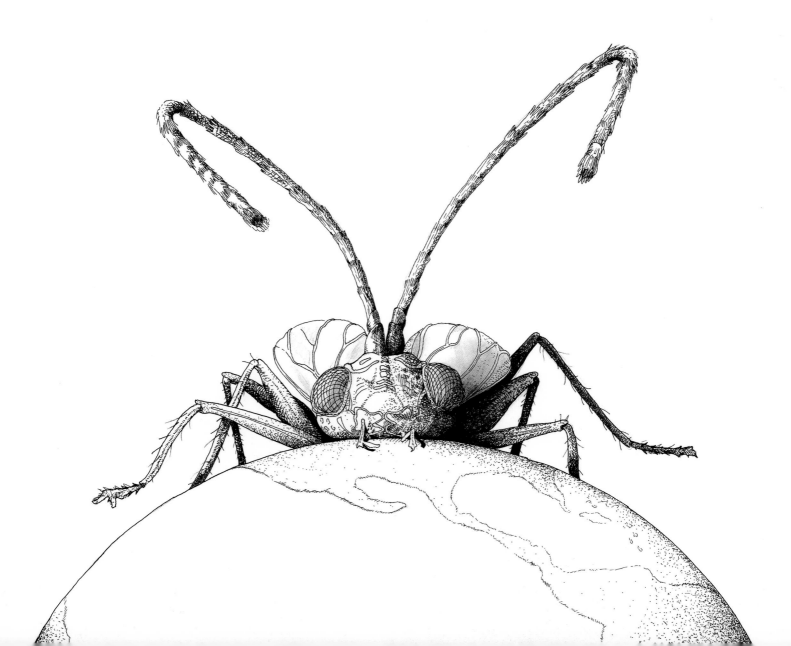

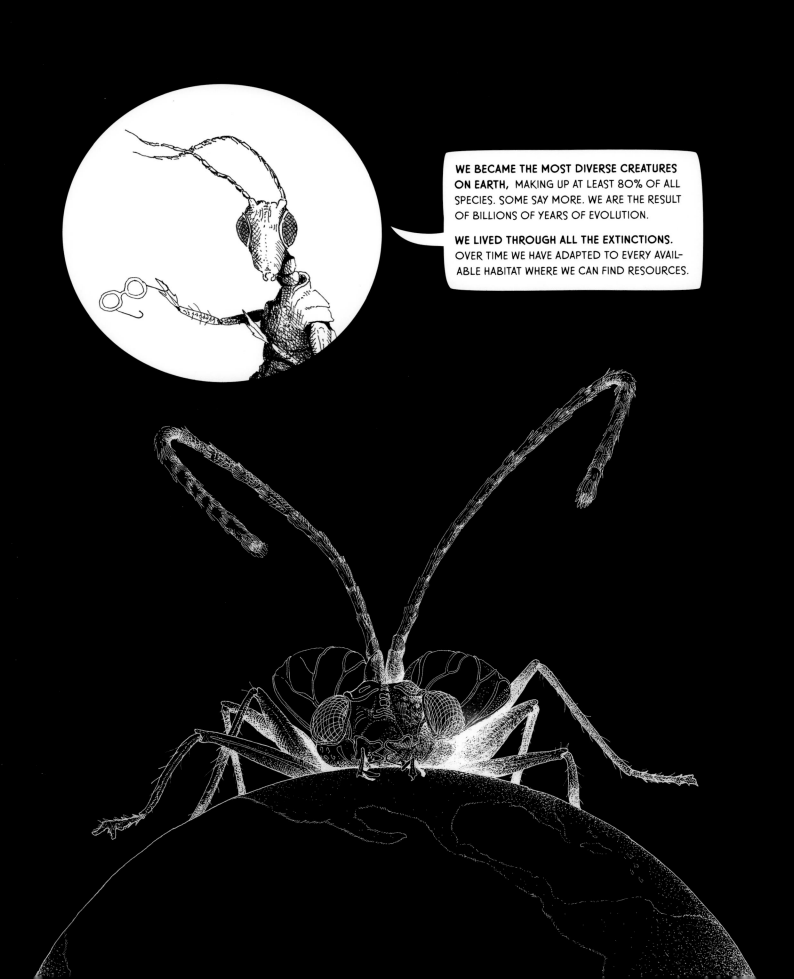

"...SCIENTISTS ESTIMATED THAT THE FIRST WINGED INSECTS APPEARED ABOUT 400 MILLION YEARS AGO AS LAND PLANTS BEGAN TO GROW SKYWARD TO FORM FOREST. IT WOULD BE ALMOST 200 MILLION YEARS BEFORE ANOTHER TYPE OF ANIMAL ACQUIRED THE ABILITY TO FLY."[1]

"INSECTS WERE THE ONLY GROUP OF INVERTEBRATES TO HAVE DEVELOPED FLIGHT. BEING ABLE TO FLY ALLOWED INSECTS TO ESCAPE PREDATORS MORE EFFECTIVELY, FIND MATES MORE EASILY AND MOVE LONG DISTANCES TO FIND THEIR FEEDING GROUNDS."[2]

TAKE THE **EVOLUTION** OF THE DRAGONFLY: "THEY HAD THE MOST ANCIENT WING STYLE...VERY SIMPLE BUT HIGHLY EFFICIENT, AND SOME MODERN INSECTS SUCH AS THE MAYFLIES AND DRAGONFLIES STILL SPORT IT."[3] THERE WERE 5,680 SPECIES OF DRAGONFLIES AND DAMSELFLIES.

"THREE HUNDRED MILLION YEARS AGO DRAGONFLIES WERE ABOUT FIVE TIMES LARGER THAN THOSE TODAY. THEIR WINGS MEASURED ABOUT 28 INCHES FROM TIP-TO-TIP."[4]

"A POSSIBLE EXPLANATION FOR THIS LARGE SIZE IS THAT THERE MAY HAVE BEEN HIGHER LEVELS OF OXYGEN IN THE ATMOSPHERE...IF OTHER GASES WERE UNCHANGED, THE EXTRA ATMOSPHERE OXYGEN WOULD HAVE MADE THE AIR DENSER THAN IT IS TODAY, MAKING FLIGHT FOR LARGER CREATURES EASIER."[5]

THIS IS AN EXAMPLE OF THE ABILITY TO ADAPT AS WELL AS EVIDENCE OF VAST CHANGES IN THE ATMOSPHERE OF GASES MILLIONS OF YEARS AGO.

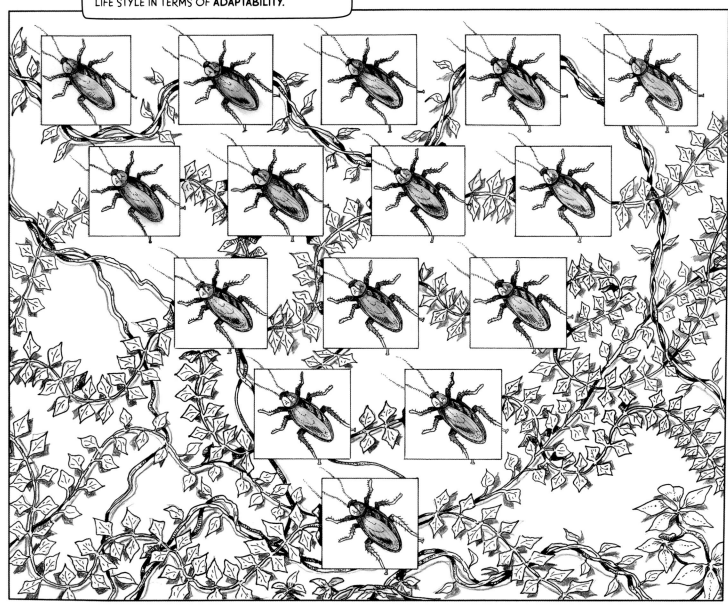

COCKROACHES, CONSISTING OF 4,500 SPECIES, SHOWED THE SIGNIFICANCE OF A SCAVENGING LIFE STYLE IN TERMS OF **ADAPTABILITY.**

"COCKROACHES WERE ABOUT 280 MILLION YEARS OLD -- 80 MILLION YEARS OLDER THAN THE FIRST DINOSAURS."[6]

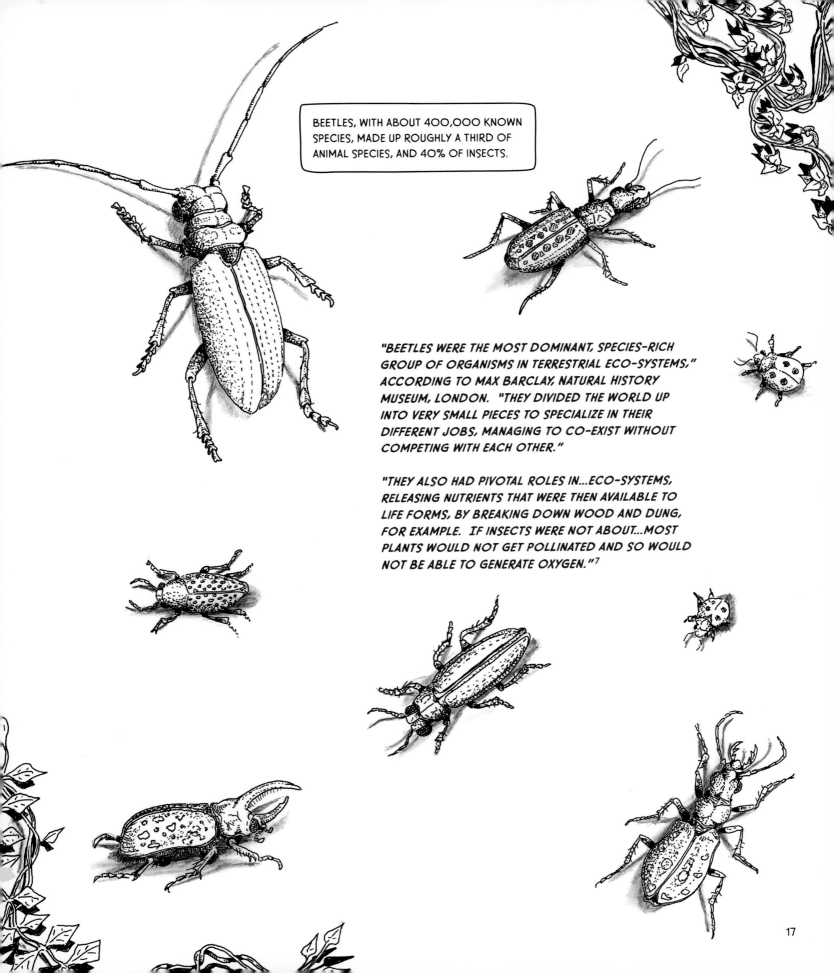

BEETLES, WITH ABOUT 400,000 KNOWN SPECIES, MADE UP ROUGHLY A THIRD OF ANIMAL SPECIES, AND 40% OF INSECTS.

"BEETLES WERE THE MOST DOMINANT, SPECIES-RICH GROUP OF ORGANISMS IN TERRESTRIAL ECO-SYSTEMS," ACCORDING TO MAX BARCLAY, NATURAL HISTORY MUSEUM, LONDON. "THEY DIVIDED THE WORLD UP INTO VERY SMALL PIECES TO SPECIALIZE IN THEIR DIFFERENT JOBS, MANAGING TO CO-EXIST WITHOUT COMPETING WITH EACH OTHER."

"THEY ALSO HAD PIVOTAL ROLES IN...ECO-SYSTEMS, RELEASING NUTRIENTS THAT WERE THEN AVAILABLE TO LIFE FORMS, BY BREAKING DOWN WOOD AND DUNG, FOR EXAMPLE. IF INSECTS WERE NOT ABOUT...MOST PLANTS WOULD NOT GET POLLINATED AND SO WOULD NOT BE ABLE TO GENERATE OXYGEN."[7]

"SMALL IS GOOD: SMALL CREATURES REQUIRED FEWER RESOURCES TO SURVIVE, THEY OCCUPIED TINIER AND INCREASINGLY SPECIALIZED NICHES, AND THEY EVOLVED MORE QUICKLY THAN LARGER ORGANISMS BECAUSE OF SHORTER GENERATION TIMES."[8]

AND THEN THERE WAS METAMORPHOSIS. THE CICADA WAS AN INTERESTING EXAMPLE. THERE WERE 4,000 SPECIES OF CICADA, WHICH EXISTED ON ALL CONTINENTS BUT ANTARCTICA. SOME LIVED UNDERGROUND (CALLED NYMPHS AT THAT STAGE) FOR MANY YEARS, AND THEN REAPPEARED. WHILE UNDERGROUND, THEY SUCKED JUICES FROM ROOTS FOR, DEPENDING ON THE SPECIES, THIRTEEN TO SEVENTEEN YEARS.

THIS IS AN EXAMPLE OF THE UNIQUENESS OF THE PROCESS OF METAMORPHOSIS.

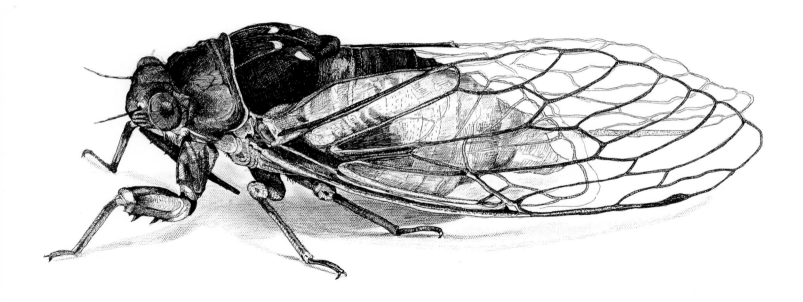

"THE EARLIEST INSECTS IN EARTH'S HISTORY DID NOT METAMORPHOSE; THEY HATCHED EGGS, ESSENTIALLY AS MINIATURE ADULTS. BETWEEN 280 MILLION AND 300 MILLION YEARS AGO, HOWEVER, SOME INSECTS BEGAN TO MATURE A LITTLE DIFFERENTLY -- THEY HATCHED IN FORMS THAT NEITHER LOOKED NOR BEHAVED LIKE THEIR ADULT VERSIONS."[9]

"HOWEVER METAMORPHOSIS EVOLVED, THE ENORMOUS NUMBERS OF METAMORPHOSING INSECTS ON THE PLANET SPEAKS FOR ITS SUCCESS AS A REPRODUCTIVE STRATEGY. THE PRIMARY ADVANTAGE OF COMPLETE METAMORPHOSIS WAS ELIMINATING COMPETITION BETWEEN YOUNG AND OLD. LARVAL INSECTS AND ADULT INSECTS OCCUPY VERY DIFFERENT ECOLOGICAL NICHES...BECAUSE LARVAE AND ADULTS DO NOT COMPETE WITH ONE ANOTHER FOR SPACE OR RESOURCES, MORE OF EACH CAN COEXIST RELATIVE TO SPECIES IN WHICH YOUNG AND OLD LIVE IN THE SAME PLACES AND EAT THE SAME THINGS."[10]

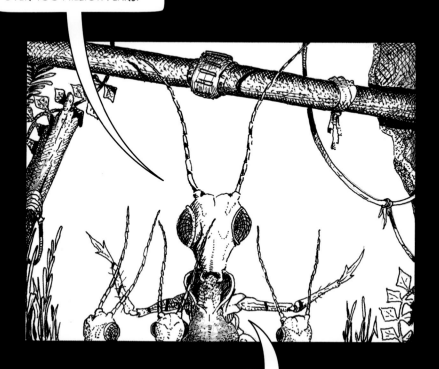

"**METAMORPHOSIS**: *THIS ALLOWED ADULTS AND LARVAE TO EXPLOIT DIFFERENT FOODS, SEASONS, HABITATS, AND LIFESTYLES (AND CLIMATE CHANGES). SO SUCCESSFUL IS COMPLETE METAMORPHOSIS, THAT IT IS PART OF THE LIFE CYCLE OF OVER 85% OF ALL INSECTS.*

SIZE: *BUGS ARE SMALL, WHICH MEANS WE CAN FIT INTO THE 'CRACKS AND CREVICES' OF NATURE. WE CAN LIVE IN SPACES TOO SMALL FOR LARGER ANIMALS AND SURVIVE ON TINY AMOUNTS OF FOOD THAT WOULD NOT SUSTAIN LARGER ANIMALS.*

WINGS: *...WINGS GREATLY IMPROVE OUR ABILITY TO ESCAPE PREDATORS, LOCATE NEW FOOD RESOURCES, MIGRATE TO NEW HABITATS AND FIND MATES.*"[11]

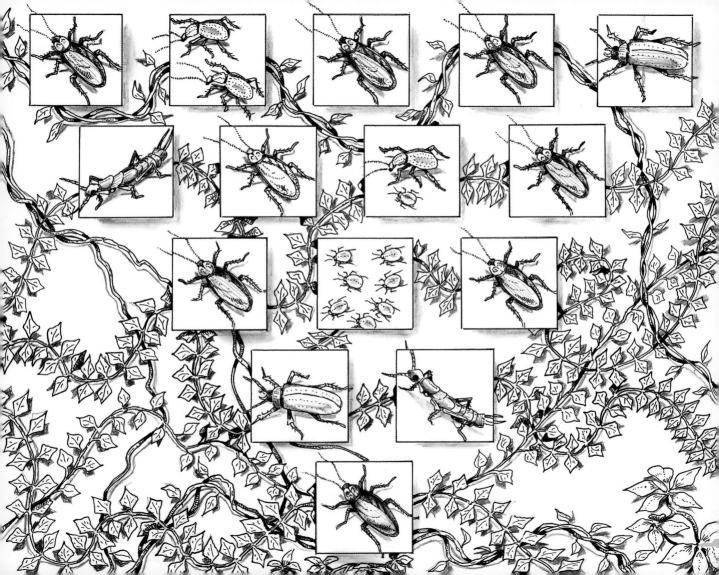

"...SCIENTISTS HAD ONLY...COME UP WITH ROUGH ESTIMATES OF THE TOTAL NUMBER OF INSECT SPECIES IN THE WORLD. AND THOSE ESTIMATES RANGED FROM 3 TO 100 MILLION SPECIES, WITH MANY AGREEING ON AN ESTIMATE OF AT LEAST 30 MILLION."[13]

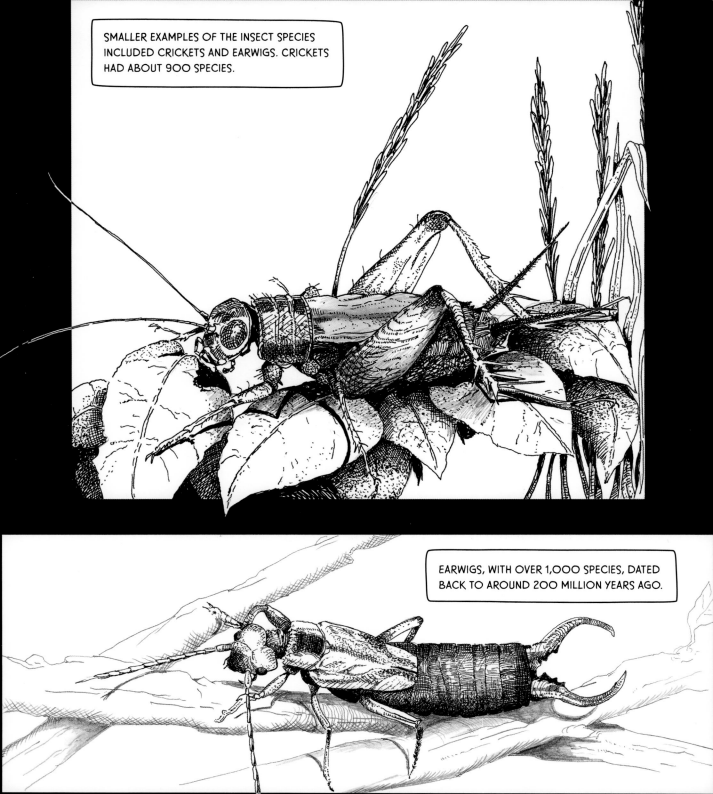

SMALLER EXAMPLES OF THE INSECT SPECIES INCLUDED CRICKETS AND EARWIGS. CRICKETS HAD ABOUT 900 SPECIES.

EARWIGS, WITH OVER 1,000 SPECIES, DATED BACK TO AROUND 200 MILLION YEARS AGO.

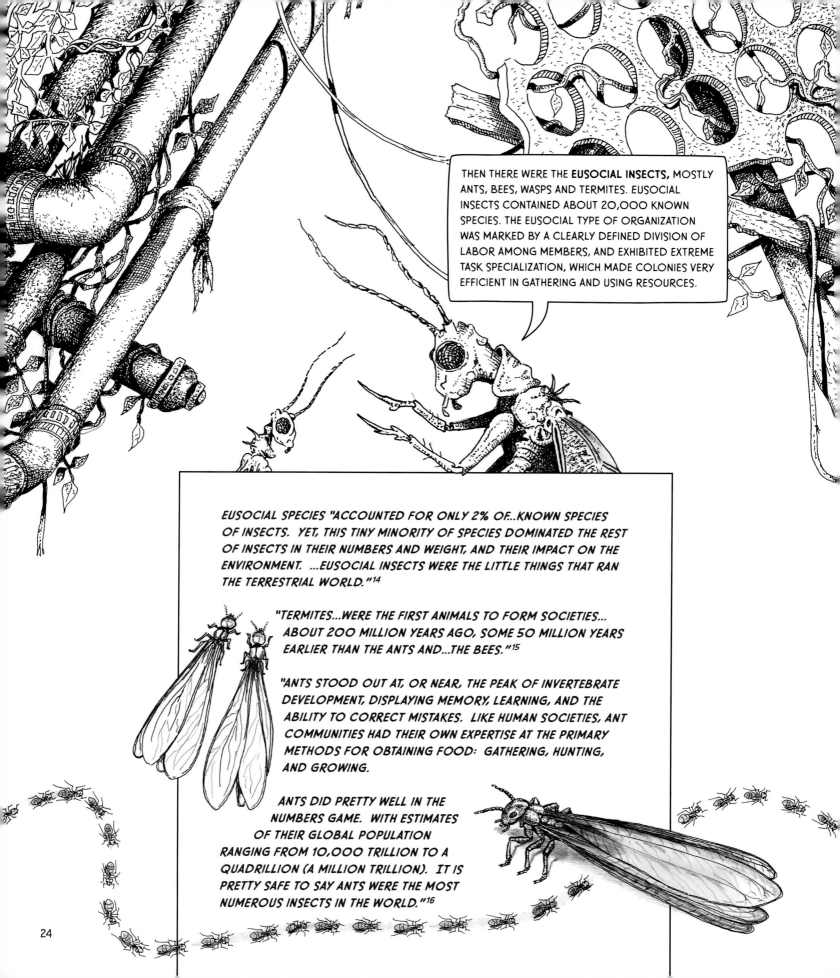

THEN THERE WERE THE **EUSOCIAL INSECTS,** MOSTLY ANTS, BEES, WASPS AND TERMITES. EUSOCIAL INSECTS CONTAINED ABOUT 20,000 KNOWN SPECIES. THE EUSOCIAL TYPE OF ORGANIZATION WAS MARKED BY A CLEARLY DEFINED DIVISION OF LABOR AMONG MEMBERS, AND EXHIBITED EXTREME TASK SPECIALIZATION, WHICH MADE COLONIES VERY EFFICIENT IN GATHERING AND USING RESOURCES.

EUSOCIAL SPECIES "ACCOUNTED FOR ONLY 2% OF...KNOWN SPECIES OF INSECTS. YET, THIS TINY MINORITY OF SPECIES DOMINATED THE REST OF INSECTS IN THEIR NUMBERS AND WEIGHT, AND THEIR IMPACT ON THE ENVIRONMENT. ...EUSOCIAL INSECTS WERE THE LITTLE THINGS THAT RAN THE TERRESTRIAL WORLD."[14]

"TERMITES...WERE THE FIRST ANIMALS TO FORM SOCIETIES... ABOUT 200 MILLION YEARS AGO, SOME 50 MILLION YEARS EARLIER THAN THE ANTS AND...THE BEES."[15]

"ANTS STOOD OUT AT, OR NEAR, THE PEAK OF INVERTEBRATE DEVELOPMENT, DISPLAYING MEMORY, LEARNING, AND THE ABILITY TO CORRECT MISTAKES. LIKE HUMAN SOCIETIES, ANT COMMUNITIES HAD THEIR OWN EXPERTISE AT THE PRIMARY METHODS FOR OBTAINING FOOD: GATHERING, HUNTING, AND GROWING.

ANTS DID PRETTY WELL IN THE NUMBERS GAME. WITH ESTIMATES OF THEIR GLOBAL POPULATION RANGING FROM 10,000 TRILLION TO A QUADRILLION (A MILLION TRILLION). IT IS PRETTY SAFE TO SAY ANTS WERE THE MOST NUMEROUS INSECTS IN THE WORLD."[16]

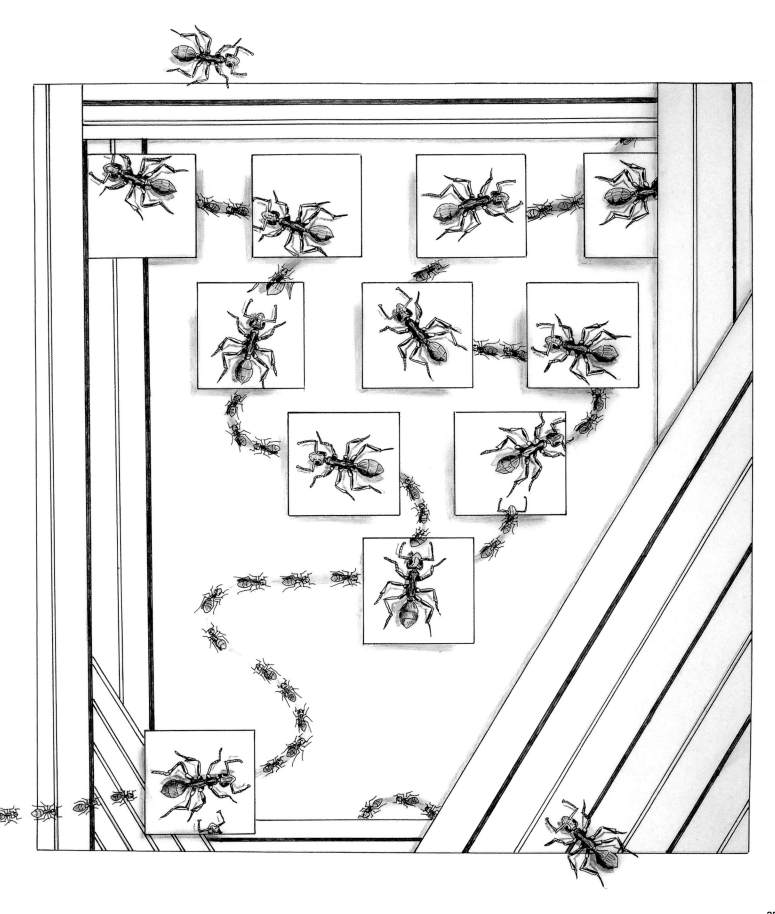

"THEY POLLINATED OVER 130 FRUITS AND VEGETABLE CROPS". OR, PUT ANOTHER WAY, AN ASTONISHING RANGE OF FRUITS AND VEGETABLE CROPS WERE 90% OR MORE RELIANT ON INSECTS FOR POLLINATION.

EXAMPLES OF PLANTS THAT WERE DEPENDENT ON BEES WERE: ALFALFA, CHERRY, CUCUMBER, SQUASH, ALMOND, APPLE, ASPARAGUS, AVOCADO, BLUEBERRY, BROCCOLI, CARROT, CAULIFLOWER, CELERY, CRANBERRY, AND ONION.[17]

BEES WERE FOUND IN EVERY HABITAT THAT CONTAINED FLOWERS.

IN THEIR EUSOCIAL WORLD, UP TO 20,000 HONEYBEES COULD LIVE IN A HIVE.

"THERE WERE AT LEAST **SEVERAL MILLION INSECT SPECIES ON THE PLANET,** AND THEY ALL HAD ONE FUNDAMENTAL COMMON FEATURE: THEY WERE UNIQUE POPULATIONS. IT'S NOT LIKE HAVING MILLIONS OF ONE SAME THING."[18]

INSECTS "...COLONIZED EARTH'S SOILS, FOREST, AND AIR BECAUSE THEY WERE THE MOST DIVERSIFIED AND BEST ADAPTED ORGANISMS TO MAKE THOSE TRANSITIONS. THE VERY SIMPLE TRAITS OF SMALL SIZE, WINGS, AND METAMORPHIC GROWTH ENSURED THAT INSECTS WERE BETTER COLONISTS AND SURVIVORS THAN ANY OTHER ORGANISM, AND **THEY PROVED THEMSELVES RESILIENT TO EVEN THE MOST CATASTROPHIC EVENTS, WHETHER IT WAS CONTINENTAL COLLISIONS, GLOBAL CLIMATE CHANGE, MASSIVE VOLCANISM, OR ASTEROID IMPACTS.**"[19]

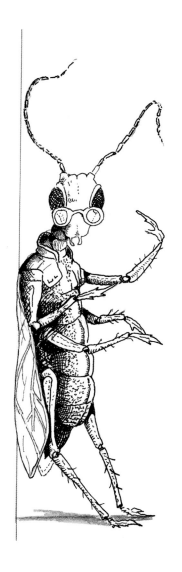

SO, FOR MORE THAN 400 MILLION YEARS **WE WERE JUST MINDING OUR OWN BUSINESS,** WHEN SUDDENLY A NEW SPECIES SHOWS UP: **HUMANS.**

CHAPTER 2:

Mankind: One species

"THE TEMPERATURE HAD HARDILY BUDGED; GLOBALLY AVERAGED, IT SWUNG IN THE NARROWEST OF RANGES BETWEEN FIFTY-EIGHT AND SIXTY DEGREES FAHRENHEIT. THAT'S WARM ENOUGH THAT THE ICE SHEETS RETREATED FROM THE CENTERS OF THE CONTINENTS SO THEY COULD GROW GRAIN, BUT COLD ENOUGH THAT MOUNTAIN GLACIERS PROVIDED DRINKING AND IRRIGATION WATER TO THOSE PLAINS AND VALLEYS YEAR ROUND...THEY BUILT THEIR GREAT CITIES NEXT TO SEAS THAT HAD REMAINED TAME AND LEVEL...THEY REFINED THE FARMING THAT SWELLED THEIR NUMBERS TO TAKE FULL ADVANTAGE OF THAT PREDICTABLE HEAT AND RAINFALL."[20]

IT WAS A SITUATION OF A **STABLE EQUILIBRIUM OF FOREST, SAVANNAS, CORAL REEFS, OCEANS, FISH, MAMMALS, AIR QUALITY, FRESH WATER AVAILABILITY, AND PRODUCTIVE SOILS.**

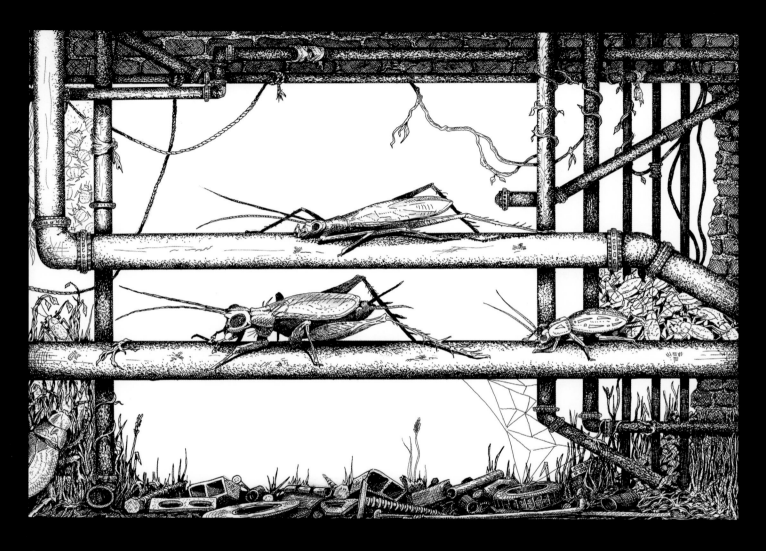

THE INDUSTRIAL REVOLUTION ORIGINATED IN ENGLAND IN THE MIDDLE OF THE EIGHTEENTH CENTURY. "FOR THE FIRST TIME... (HUMANS) MOVED BEYOND AGRICULTURE...TO INDUSTRY (AS THE) ECONOMIC BASE."[21] NEW TECHNOLOGIES -- THE STEAM ENGINE, MECHANICAL SPINNING AND WEAVING, LARGE SCALE STEEL PRODUCTION -- ALL SPAWNED THIS NEW CHAPTER.

"THE STEAM ENGINE MADE POSSIBLE NEW FORMS OF TRANSPORTATION...INCLUDING STEAM POWERED RAILROADS AND STEAM POWERED OCEAN FREIGHTERS. THE (NEW) ENERGY ALSO ALLOW(ED) A FAR GREATER SCALE OF INDUSTRIAL TRANSFORMATION OF MATERIALS THAN EVER BEFORE. THE PRODUCTION OF STEEL SOARED, AND THIS IN TURN MADE POSSIBLE THE MASSIVE EXPANSION OF CITIES, INDUSTRIES, AND INFRASTRUCTURE OF ALL KINDS."[22]

COAL, GAS, AND OIL, WHICH WERE ABUNDANT AND THE ENERGY SOURCE FUELING INDUSTRIAL GROWTH, CREATED **A SERIOUS ISSUE FOR HUMANS,** AND FOR US.

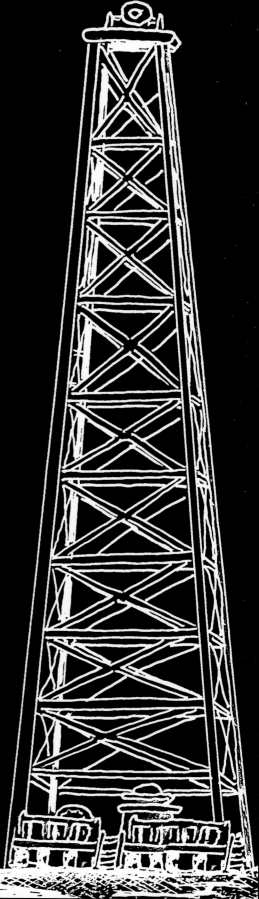

THE MAIN SOURCE OF HUMAN INDUCED CARBON DIOXIDE CAME FROM BURNING COAL, OIL, AND GAS.

OVER SEVERAL CENTURIES "BURNING COAL (AND NATURAL GAS, AND PETROLEUM) HAD UNWITTINGLY CAUSED HUMANS TO CHANGE THE CLIMATE OF THEIR WORLD AND SET IN MOTION FEEDBACK LOOPS THAT WERE GOING TO BE VERY DIFFICULT TO TAMP DOWN. THERE WAS ALREADY AN ENORMOUS AMOUNT OF CARBON DIOXIDE IN OUR AIR THAT WOULD BE THERE FOR THOUSANDS OF YEARS TO COME AND KEEP OUR WORLD WARMER THAN IT WOULD HAVE BEEN."[23]

DEFORESTATION WAS A PROBLEM AS WELL.

"TREES ARE GOOD AT KEEPING CARBON DIOXIDE OUT OF THE AIR...**FORESTS ARE A CRUCIAL 'CARBON SINK,' LIVING ENGINES FOR ABSORBING AND STORING CARBON.** TROPICAL FORESTS STORE THE MOST CARBON OF ALL, AND NO TROPICAL FOREST ON EARTH WAS BIGGER THAN THE AMAZON. IT ACCOUNTED FOR ABOUT HALF OF ALL THE CARBON THESE FORESTS STORED. BUT THE AMAZON HAD LOST NEARLY A FIFTH OF ITS FOREST COVER."[24]

"...**DEFORESTATION (IN 2016) ADDED...20% OR MORE OF...(CARBON TO THE ATMOSPHERE)**"[25]

INDONESIAN FOREST FIRES PROVIDED ANOTHER STRIKING EXAMPLE. IN 2015 "...AT LEAST 2 MILLION HECTARES OF FOREST WERE BURNED. ...GREENHOUSE GASES RELEASED BY THOSE FIRES EXCEEDED THE EMISSIONS OF THE ENTIRE AMERICAN ECONOMY."

"BETWEEN 2001 AND 2014, THE COUNTRY LOST 18.5 MILLION HECTARES OF TREE COVER -- AN AREA TWICE THE SIZE OF IRELAND. IN 2014, INDONESIA OVERTOOK BRAZIL TO BECOME THE WORLD'S BIGGEST DEFORESTER."[26]

"AND WHILE INDONESIA AND BRAZIL REMAINED THE WORLD'S LEADERS IN THE LOSS OF TROPICAL FOREST, SMALLER NATIONS SUCH AS CAMBODIA, SIERRA LEONE AND MADAGASCAR WERE CONTRIBUTING MORE TO THE OVER ALL TOTAL...(AS WERE) BOLIVIA, PERU AND VENEZUELA..."[27]

ANOTHER POINT: "THROUGH PHOTOSYNTHESIS, PLANTS PROVIDE THE OXYGEN WE BREATH... OF THE MORE THAN 300,000 KNOWN SPECIES OF PLANTS, **ABOUT 68% OF EVALUATED PLANT SPECIES WERE THREATENED WITH EXTINCTION.**"[28]

ANOTHER SOURCE OF DEFORESTATION **WAS STRIP AND OPEN PIT MINING.**

STRIP MINING FOR COAL WAS WELL KNOWN, BUT THERE WERE OTHER REASONS FOR THESE TYPES OF MINES: RARE EARTH MINERALS AND PHOSPHATE, FOR EXAMPLE.

"FROM SMART PHONES TO THE LATEST WEAPONRY, THE TECHNOLOGY THAT UNDERPINNED MODERN LIFE WOULD HAVE BEEN IMPOSSIBLE WITHOUT RARE EARTH MINERALS. ...A STUDY FROM RESEARCHERS AT YALE HAD FOUND THAT MANY OF THE MATERIALS USED IN HIGH-TECH PRODUCTS, INCLUDING RARE EARTH METALS, HAD NO SATISFACTORY SUBSTITUTES..."[29]

"HOW LONG WOULD ECONOMICAL RESOURCES OF KEY MINERALS LAST IF EVERY HUMAN ON THE PLANET CONSUMED EVEN HALF AS MUCH AS THE AVERAGE RICH-WORLD CITIZEN IN 2016? ...THE WORLD SUPPLY OF ANTIMONY, TO NAME ONE MINERAL, WOULD RUN OUT IN ONLY TEN YEARS. SILVER COULD BE GONE IN LESS THAT FIVE. AND INDIUM COULD BE USED UP IN ONLY A FEW YEARS."[30]

"MODERN AGRICULTURE DEPENDED ON A STEADY SUPPLY OF PHOSPHATE FERTILIZER
PRODUCED BY MINING PHOSPHATE ROCK. (HUMANITY PASSED THE PEAK OF AVAILABLE
PHOSPHATE RESOURCES MID-21ST CENTURY) OVERUSE...WAS (A) PRIMARY DRIVER OF
ALGAE BLOOMS (DUE TO RUN-OFF INTO THE WATER SYSTEM) THAT CAUSED TOXICITY,
OXYGEN LOSS, FISH KILLS...CAUSING MASSIVE DAMAGE TO AQUATIC ECO SYSTEMS,
FRESHWATER RESOURCES, AND COASTAL AREAS."[31]

ALL OF THE PRECEDING WAS CAUSING CO2 LEVELS TO RISE AT AN ALARMING AND **INCREASING RATE.** THEY WENT FROM 280 PARTS PER MILLION (PPM) IN PRE-INDUSTRIAL TIMES TO 370 PPM IN THE 1980S, TO 400 PPM IN 2014, TO A SURE, IMMINENT PATH TO 420 PPM. THESE LEVELS WERE EVIDENT IN THE TIME OF THE DINOSAURS, BUT **NEVER HAD THEY INCREASED SO FAST.**

"GLOBAL GHG (GREENHOUSE GASES OF WHICH 76% ARE CARBON DIOXIDE) EMISSIONS DUE TO HUMAN ACTIVITIES HAD GROWN SINCE PRE-INDUSTRIAL TIMES, WITH AN INCREASE OF 70% BETWEEN 1970 AND 2004. WARMING OF THE CLIMATE SYSTEM WAS UNEQUIVOCAL, AS WAS NEW EVIDENCE FROM OBSERVATIONS IN INCREASES IN GLOBAL AIR AND OCEAN TEMPERATURES, WIDESPREAD MELTING OF SNOW AND ICE, AND RAISING GLOBAL SEA LEVELS."[32]

"...MODERN SOCIETY WAS BUILT AROUND A SPECIFIC KIND OF CLIMATE AND A SPECIFIC LEVEL OF CARBON DIOXIDE."[33] THE DRAMATIC RATE OF CHANGE OF CARBON DIOXIDE IN THE AIR WAS THE THREAT, AS WELL AS WHAT THAT SPEED OF CHANGE IGNITED.

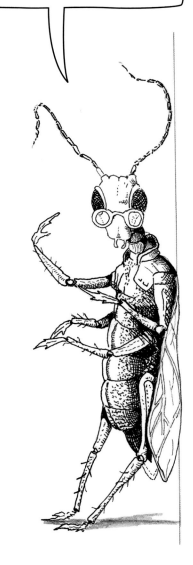

ADDITIONALLY, CITIES SAW THE PHYSICAL EVIDENCE OF POLLUTION IN DAILY LIFE. RATHER THAN EXPRESSING OUTRAGE OR TAKING ACTION, THEY SEEMED TO SIMPLY ACCEPT THE HEALTH HAZARDS, DONNING FACE MASKS OR SHUTTING DOORS AND WINDOWS.

"IT WASN'T JUST SWEATERS THAT KINDERGARTNERS WERE WEARING AS SOON AS THEY POURED OUT OF THEIR CLASSROOMS...IN INDIA'S CAPITAL CITY. THEY WERE ALSO WEARING MASKS. ...AS PEOPLE IN BEIJING AND OTHER HEAVILY POLLUTED ASIAN CITIES HAD ALREADY DONE."[34]

*"ABOUT 5.5 MILLION PEOPLE AROUND THE WORLD DIED PREMATURELY EVERY YEAR FROM BREATHING POLLUTED AIR. ...**92% OF PEOPLE BREATHED WHAT WAS CLASSIFIED AS UNHEALTHY AIR.** ...EVEN IN THE ABSENSE OF AIR POLLUTION EPISODES, THE CONCENTRATION OF PARTICLES SUSPENDED IN THE AIR EXCEEDED WHAT WAS CONSIDERED TO BE ACCEPTABLE..."[35]*

BEIJING HAD BEEN HIT WITH A TOXIC CLOUD WITH THE "CONCENTRATION OF FINE, DEADLY PARTICULATE MATTER...(HITTING) 40 TIMES THE EXPOSURE LIMIT RECOMMENDED BY THE WORLD HEALTH ORGANIZATION."[36]

AND THEN THERE WAS THE **MELTING ICE**.

"TWO GROUPS OF RESEARCHERS -- ONE FROM NASA'S JET PROPULSION LAB AND THE OTHER FROM THE UNIVERSITY OF WASHINGTON -- CONCLUDED THAT A SEGMENT OF THE WEST ANTARCTIC ICE SHEET HAD GONE INTO 'IRREVERSIBLE DECLINE.' THE SEGMENT...CONTAINED ENOUGH WATER TO RAISE GLOBAL SEA LEVELS BY FOUR FEET, AND ITS MELTING WOULD DESTABILIZE OTHER PARTS OF THE ICE SHEET, WHICH HELD ENOUGH ICE TO ADD TEN MORE FEET."[37]

OVER 40 YEARS (SINCE 1976), ARCTIC SEA ICE (AS OPPOSED TO ICE ON LAND, KNOWN AS SHEET ICE) HAD BEEN DECREASING AT A RATE OF ABOUT 5% A DECADE.

"...THE LOSS OF THIS ICE (SHEET AND SEA) WAS A VERY TROUBLESOME THING: WITHOUT ICE, THEY WERE LOOKING AT WARMING SEAS, SEA LIFE DIE-OFFS, AND DISRUPTION OF ANCIENT OCEAN CURRENTS, WHICH WOULD LEAD TO DISRUPTION OF WEATHER PATTERNS EVERYWHERE. BECAUSE OF THE POSITIVE FEEDBACK NATURE OF THE INTERACTION OF THE AIR, THE ICE, AND SEA, THINGS WERE GOING TO START CHANGING FASTER AND FASTER. *...HUMANKIND WAS CHANGING THE OCEAN, AND THE OCEAN WAS BIG ENOUGH TO CHANGE EVERYTHING.*"[38]

GLOBAL WARMING MELTS ICE. IN ANTARCTICA, MELTING GLACIERS EXPOSED LAND; LAND ABSORBED **WARMTH**, WHICH UNDERCUT GLACIERS, WHICH REGRESSED FURTHER INLAND CREATING MORE EXPOSED LAND AND MORE MELTING.

YOU WOULD HAVE THOUGHT WHEN HUMANS SAW THAT THERE WASN'T ENOUGH SNOW FOR THE IDITAROD SLED RACE, THAT ESKIMOS WERE WEARING BERMUDA SHORTS, AND THAT THE MELTING ICE WAS NOT SUPPORTING THE LIVES OF POLAR BEARS, THEY WOULD HAVE FIGURED SOMETHING WAS UP.

POLITICIANS AND BUSINESSES APPARENTLY DIDN'T WANT TO TALK ABOUT RISING SEA LEVELS IN KEY REAL ESTATE AREAS BECAUSE THEY DIDN'T WANT TO SCARE INVESTORS, FEARFUL THAT MORTGAGES AND INSURANCE WOULD NOT BE AVAILABLE, BOND OFFERINGS WOULD FAIL AND THAT REAL ESTATE AND BUSINESS TAXES WOULD PLUMMET.

"...MANY CORNERSTONE ELEMENTS OF OUR CLIMATE BEGAN CHANGING FAR FASTER THAN MOST SCIENTISTS HAD PROJECTED. THE ARCTIC BEGAN LOSING SEA ICE SEVERAL DECADES AHEAD OF EVERY SINGLE CLIMATE MODEL USED BY THE IPCC (INTERGOVERNMENTAL PANEL ON CLIMATE CHANGE), WHICH IN TURN MEANT THAT THE ARCTIC REGION WARMED UP EVEN FASTER THAN SCIENTISTS HAD EXPECTED. AT THE SAME TIME, THE GREAT ICE SHEETS OF GREEN-LAND AND ANTARCTICA, HAD BEGUN DISINTEGRATING A CENTURY AHEAD OF SCHEDULE."[39]

IT WAS PREDICTED THAT BY 2030, $69 BILLION IN COASTAL PROPERTY IN FLORIDA WILL FLOOD AT HIGH TIDE.[40]

"THE U.S. ARMY CORPS OF ENGINEERS PROJECTED THAT THEY (WATER LEVELS IN THE MIAMI AREA) COULD RISE BY AS MUCH AS FIVE FEET (BY THE END OF THE 21ST CENTURY); THE NATIONAL OCEANIC AND ATMOSPHERIC ADMINISTRATION PREDICTED UP TO SIX AND A HALF FEET. THE CHAIRMAN OF THE UNIVERSITY OF MIAMI GEOLOGICAL-SCIENCE DEPARTMENT THOUGHT ALL THESE PROJECTIONS WERE PROBABLY LOW. 'MANY GEOLOGISTS WERE LOOKING AT THE POSSIBILITY OF A TEN-TO-THIRTY FOOT RANGE BY THE END OF THE CENTURY.'"[41]

"...AS THE WATER ROSE, (IT) BUBBLED UP THROUGH THE STORM DRAINS. AS THAT HAPPENED MORE OFTEN, IT CAUSED MORE THAN A MILLION SEPTIC TANKS IN THE AREA TO BURST, AND...CONTAMINATED THE GROUND WATER."[42]

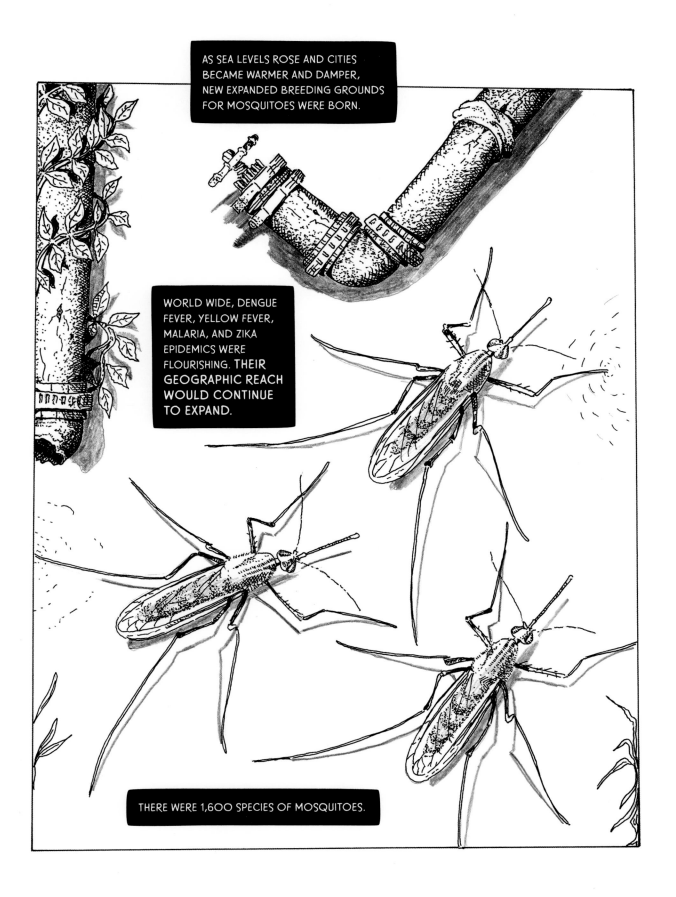

AS SEA LEVELS ROSE AND CITIES BECAME WARMER AND DAMPER, NEW EXPANDED BREEDING GROUNDS FOR MOSQUITOES WERE BORN.

WORLD WIDE, DENGUE FEVER, YELLOW FEVER, MALARIA, AND ZIKA EPIDEMICS WERE FLOURISHING. **THEIR GEOGRAPHIC REACH WOULD CONTINUE TO EXPAND.**

THERE WERE 1,600 SPECIES OF MOSQUITOES.

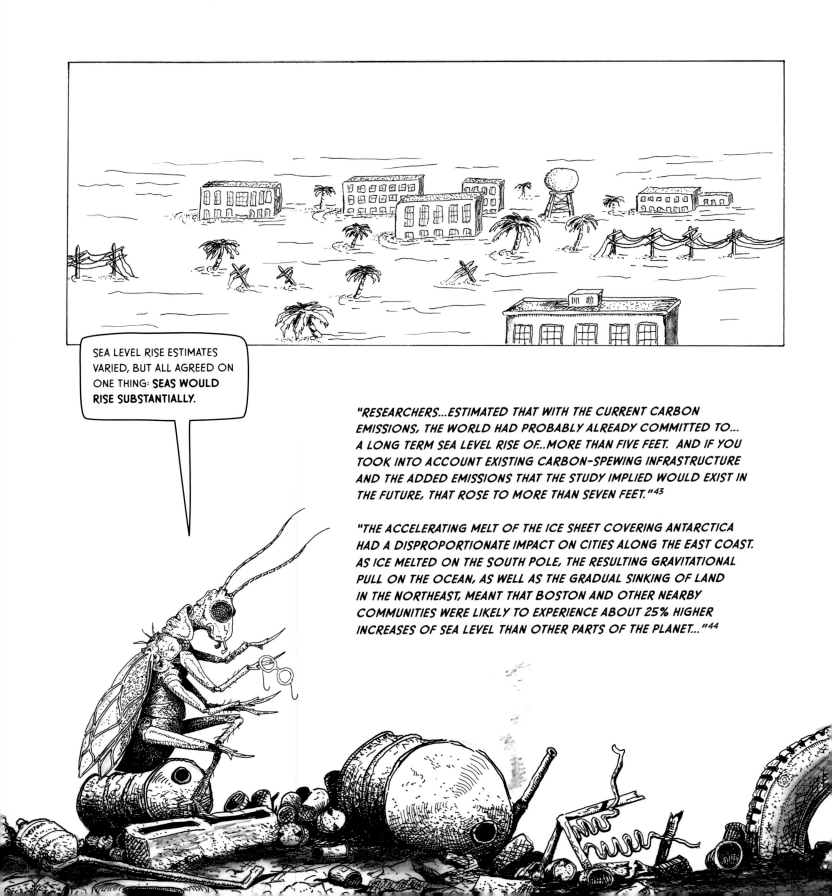

SEA LEVEL RISE ESTIMATES VARIED, BUT ALL AGREED ON ONE THING: **SEAS WOULD RISE SUBSTANTIALLY.**

"RESEARCHERS...ESTIMATED THAT WITH THE CURRENT CARBON EMISSIONS, THE WORLD HAD PROBABLY ALREADY COMMITTED TO... A LONG TERM SEA LEVEL RISE OF...MORE THAN FIVE FEET. AND IF YOU TOOK INTO ACCOUNT EXISTING CARBON-SPEWING INFRASTRUCTURE AND THE ADDED EMISSIONS THAT THE STUDY IMPLIED WOULD EXIST IN THE FUTURE, THAT ROSE TO MORE THAN SEVEN FEET."[43]

"THE ACCELERATING MELT OF THE ICE SHEET COVERING ANTARCTICA HAD A DISPROPORTIONATE IMPACT ON CITIES ALONG THE EAST COAST. AS ICE MELTED ON THE SOUTH POLE, THE RESULTING GRAVITATIONAL PULL ON THE OCEAN, AS WELL AS THE GRADUAL SINKING OF LAND IN THE NORTHEAST, MEANT THAT BOSTON AND OTHER NEARBY COMMUNITIES WERE LIKELY TO EXPERIENCE ABOUT 25% HIGHER INCREASES OF SEA LEVEL THAN OTHER PARTS OF THE PLANET..."[44]

RICE WAS ONE OF THE MOST IMPORTANT FOOD STAPLES FOR MORE THAN HALF THE WORLD'S POPULATION. RISING SEA LEVELS, CAUSING SALT WATER INTRUSION, A CONSEQUENCE OF CLIMATE CHANGE, CONTRIBUTED TO THE DRASTIC DECLINE IN PRODUCTION.

"THE COMING DECADES, THE WORLD BANK PREDICTED, WOULD SEE POLITICAL INSTABILITY, FOOD SHORTAGES, AND FAMINE, LEADING TO DISPLACEMENT OF MILLIONS OF PEOPLE. SOUTH ASIA'S AND SOUTHEAST ASIA'S HEAVILY POPULATED COASTS, PARTICULARLY THOSE IN BANGLADESH AND VIETNAM, WOULD BE INUNDATED. WORSE, **RISING SEAS WOULD INVADE MAJOR DELTAS, POISONING THEM WITH SALT WATER** AND DESTROYING SOME OF THE WORLD'S RICHEST AGRICULTURAL LAND. THE MEKONG RIVER DELTA IN VIETNAM, WHERE 17 MILLION PEOPLE LIVED AND HALF THE COUNTRY'S RICE SUPPLY WAS GROWN, WAS ALREADY BATTLING SALT WATER INTRUSION."[45]

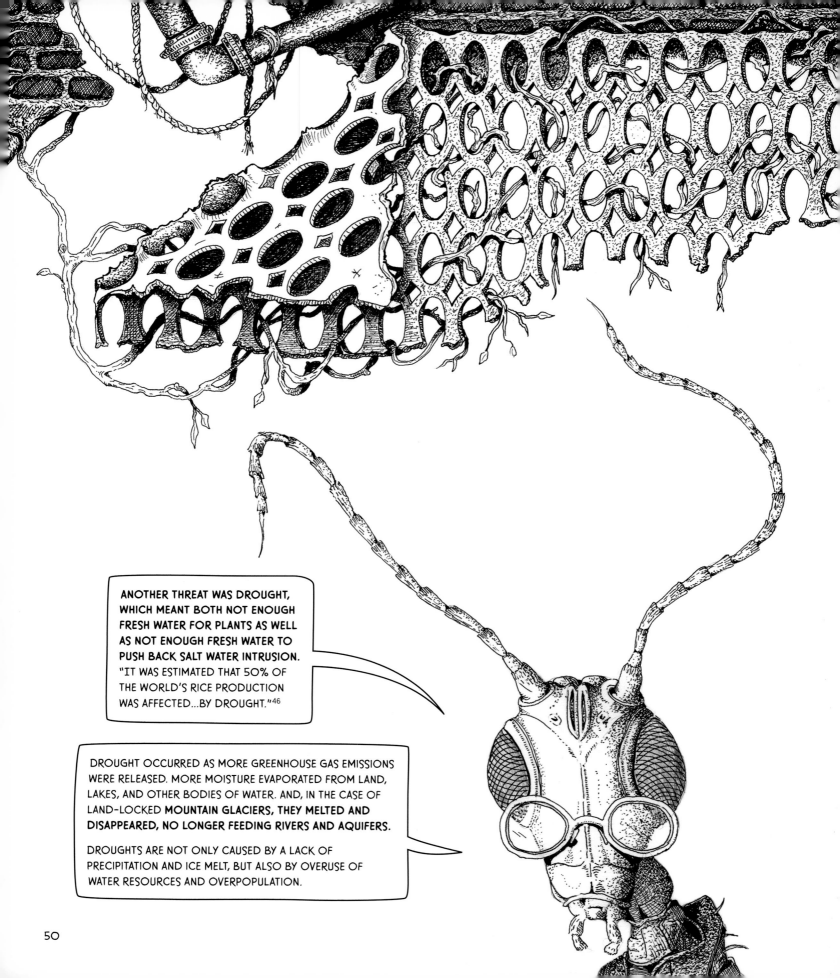

ANOTHER THREAT WAS DROUGHT,
WHICH MEANT BOTH NOT ENOUGH
FRESH WATER FOR PLANTS AS WELL
AS NOT ENOUGH FRESH WATER TO
PUSH BACK SALT WATER INTRUSION.
"IT WAS ESTIMATED THAT 50% OF
THE WORLD'S RICE PRODUCTION
WAS AFFECTED...BY DROUGHT."[46]

DROUGHT OCCURRED AS MORE GREENHOUSE GAS EMISSIONS
WERE RELEASED. MORE MOISTURE EVAPORATED FROM LAND,
LAKES, AND OTHER BODIES OF WATER. AND, IN THE CASE OF
LAND-LOCKED **MOUNTAIN GLACIERS**, THEY MELTED AND
DISAPPEARED, NO LONGER FEEDING RIVERS AND AQUIFERS.

DROUGHTS ARE NOT ONLY CAUSED BY A LACK OF
PRECIPITATION AND ICE MELT, BUT ALSO BY OVERUSE OF
WATER RESOURCES AND OVERPOPULATION.

WHEN RAIN DID COME TO DROUGHT STRICKEN AREAS, THE DRY, HARDENED **SOILS WERE UNABLE TO ABSORB WATER.**

"THE REGION KNOWN AS THE 'THIRD POLE'...ENCOMPASSED THE HIMALAYA AND HINDU KUSH MOUNTAIN RANGE AND THE TIBETAN PLATEAU...THIS REGION WAS THE SOURCE OF THE 10 MAJOR RIVER SYSTEMS THAT PROVIDED IRRIGATION, POWER, AND DRINKING WATER FOR OVER 1.5 BILLION PEOPLE IN ASIA AND NEARLY 20% OF THE WORLD'S POPULATION."[47]

IN INDIA, "EVERY DAY BROUGHT NEWS OF EXHAUSTED RIVERS AND WELLS, DESTITUTE FARMERS MIGRATING TO THE CITIES OR EVEN COMMITTING SUICIDE, WATER TRAINS BEING DISPATCHED TO PARCHED REGIONS -- AND OF LEOPARDS VENTURING INTO TOWNS IN SEARCH OF A DRINK.

INDIA RELIED...ON UNDERGROUND AQUIFERS FOR SOME TWO-THIRDS OF ITS IRRIGATION AND FOR MORE THAN THREE QUARTERS OF ITS DRINKING WATER. WITH 30 MILLION WELLS AND PUMPS AT WORK...GROUND WATER LEVELS HAD BEEN DROPPING. NEARLY TWO-THIRDS OF WELLS TESTED...SHOWED LEVELS LOWER THAN THEIR TEN-YEAR AVERAGE."[48]

ACCORDING TO THE CHINESE ACADEMY OF SCIENCE IN 2015, THE TIBETAN PLATEAU WAS ALREADY WARMING TWO TIMES FASTER THAT THE GLOBAL AVERAGE.

THE WATERS FLOWING FROM THE "...46,000 GLACIERS OF THE THIRD POLE REGION... REACHED PLACES AS DISTANT AS THE TROPICAL MEKONG DELTA OF VIETNAM, THE HILLS OF EASTERN MYANMAR AND THE SOUTH PLAIN OF BANGLADESH. ...THESE GLACIERS WERE RECEDING AT AN EVER-QUICKENING PACE... AND THREATENING ASIA'S WATER SUPPLY."[49]

"IN NORTHWEST CHINA THERE WERE 300 MILLION PEOPLE RELYING ON SNOW MELT FOR WATER SUPPLY. THERE'S NO WAY TO REPLACE IT UNTIL THE NEXT ICE AGE."[50]

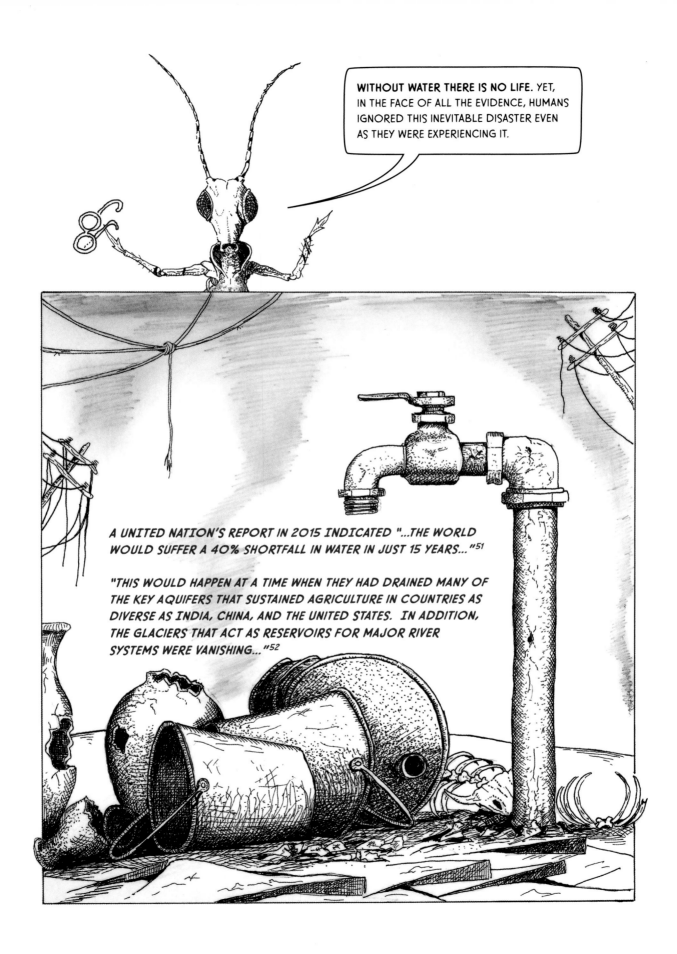

"A NASA STUDY...PROVIDED AUTHORITATIVE ESTIMATES OF THE STATE OF 37 MAJOR AQUIFERS AROUND THE GLOBE. USING SATELLITES...RESEARCHERS FOUND THAT 21 OF THESE AQUIFERS WERE BEING DEPLETED."[53]

A 2012 WORLD BANK REPORT SAID, "DROUGHT AFFECTED AREAS WOULD INCREASE FROM 15.4% OF GLOBAL CROPLAND TODAY, TO AROUND 44% BY 2100. THE MOST SEVERELY AFFECTED REGIONS IN THE NEXT 30 TO 90 YEARS WOULD BE IN SOUTHERN AFRICA, THE UNITED STATES, SOUTHERN EUROPE AND SOUTHEAST ASIA."[54]

"AN ANNUAL REPORT FROM THE MINISTRY OF WATER RESOURCES (CHINA) SAID THAT IN 2014, NEARLY HALF OF 2,071 MONITORED WELLS HAD 'QUITE POOR' WATER QUALITY, AND AN ADDITIONAL 36% HAD 'EXTREMELY POOR' QUALITY." IT FOUND "...THAT 32.9% OF WELLS IN NORTHERN AND CENTRAL CHINA HAD WATER...FIT ONLY FOR INDUSTRIAL USES...AN ADDITIONAL 47.3% OF WELLS WERE EVEN WORSE. THE HEAVY CONTAMINATION OF SUPPLIES NEAR THE SURFACE WAS FORCING MORE CITIES TO DIG THOUSANDS OF FEET UNDER GROUND FOR CLEAN WATER, AND THAT WAS TAXING THE CAPACITY OF THOSE DEEP AQUIFERS..."[55]

...THE PLANET KEPT GETTING WARMER AND WARMER.

THE RATE OF WARMING SINCE 1990 HAD INCREASED 50% RELATIVE TO THE LONGER TREND, MEASURED SINCE 1880.[56]

"IN THE 136 YEARS SCIENTISTS (HAD) BEEN TRACKING GLOBAL TEMPERATURES...2016 (WAS) THE HOTTEST YEAR EVER RECORDED--BREAKING RECORDS SET THE TWO PREVIOUS YEARS."[57]

"FOURTEEN OF THE 15 HOTTEST YEARS HAD OCCURRED SINCE 2000, AS HEAT WAVES HAD BECOME MORE FREQUENT, MORE INTENSE AND LONGER LASTING."[58]

FREQUENT INTENSE RAINFALL EVENTS, WIND AND FLOODING WERE THE PRODUCT OF MORE WATER VAPOR IN THE ATMOSPHERE. THIS WAS DUE TO SUBSTANTIAL WARMING OF SURFACE TEMPERATURES."[59]

WITH CLIMATE CHANGE IMPACTING AGRICULTURAL PRODUCTION, PEOPLE NECESSARILY NEEDED TO RELY MORE ON FISH FOR THEIR NUTRITIONAL NEEDS. BUT **HUMANS HAD ALREADY IMPACTED THE OCEAN.**

OCEANS WERE ACIDIFYING FASTER THAN THEY HAD OVER THE LAST 300 MILLION YEARS, DURING WHICH TIME THERE WERE FOUR MAJOR EXTINCTIONS DRIVEN BY NATURAL BURSTS OF CARBON.

"OCEAN ACIDIFICATION IS IRREVERSIBLE ON TIME SCALES OF AT LEAST TEN THOUSAND YEARS. THE SEA WAS ALREADY 30% MORE ACID THAN AT ANY TIME IN THE LAST EIGHT HUNDRED YEARS."[60]

OCEAN ACIDIFICATION RESULTS FROM A REDUCTION IN THE PH (THE LOWER THE PH THE MORE ACIDIC) OF THE OCEAN CAUSED BY AN UPTAKE OF THE CARBON DIOXIDE FROM THE ATMOSPHERE.

"OCEAN ACIDIFICATION IS SOMETIMES REFERRED TO AS GLOBAL WARMING'S 'EQUAL TWIN.'"[61]

THE NATIONAL OCEANIC AND ATMOSPHERIC ADMINISTRATION (NOAA) ESTIMATED IN 2016 THAT 20% OF CORAL REEFS WERE ALREADY DAMAGED BEYOND RECOVERY (DUE TO ACIDIFICATION) AND THAT 50% WERE IN CRITICAL CONDITION. AT THE 70% LEVEL, THAT WOULD RISK THE COLLAPSE OF THE ENTIRE ECOSYSTEM AS IT PROVIDES FOOD AND SHELTER TO A QUARTER OF ALL MARINE SPECIES, WHICH IN TURN SUPPORTS OTHER FISH STOCKS.

OVER-FISHING WAS ALSO HAVING AN IMPACT. "BOTTOM TRAWLERS SCRAPING LARGE NETS ACROSS THE SEA FLOOR HAD ALREADY AFFECTED 20 MILLION SQUARE MILES OF OCEAN, TURNING PARTS OF THE CONTINENTAL SHELF INTO RUBBLE.

MINING OPERATIONS, TOO, WERE POISED TO TRANSFORM THE OCEAN. CONTRACTS FOR SEABED MINING COVERED 460,000 SQUARE MILES UNDERWATER...UP FROM ZERO IN 2000. SEABED MINING HAD THE POTENTIAL TO TEAR UP UNIQUE ECOSYSTEMS AND INTRODUCE MORE POLLUTION INTO THE DEEP SEA."[62]

THE CENTER FOR BIOLOGICAL DIVERSITY IN 2010 STATED THAT 1,851 SPECIES OF FISH -- 21% OF ALL FISH SPECIES EVALUATED -- WERE DEEMED AT RISK OF EXTINCTION. ADDITION-ALLY, THE WORLD WILDLIFE FUND CALCULATED THAT MORE THAN **85% OF THE WORLD'S FISHERIES HAD BEEN PUSHED TO OR BEYOND THEIR BIOLOGICAL LIMITS.**

THE GLOBAL FISHING FLEET, THEY SAID, WAS TWO TO THREE TIMES LARGER THAN WHAT THE OCEANS COULD SUSTAINABLY SUPPORT.

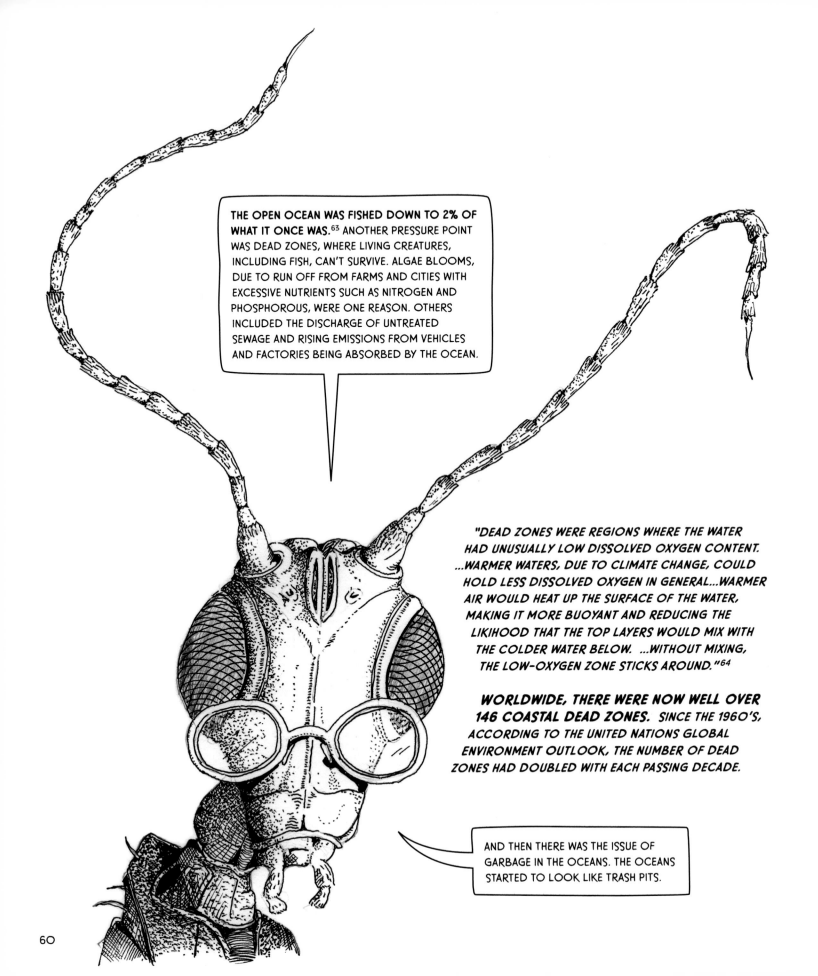

THE OPEN OCEAN WAS FISHED DOWN TO 2% OF WHAT IT ONCE WAS.[63] ANOTHER PRESSURE POINT WAS DEAD ZONES, WHERE LIVING CREATURES, INCLUDING FISH, CAN'T SURVIVE. ALGAE BLOOMS, DUE TO RUN OFF FROM FARMS AND CITIES WITH EXCESSIVE NUTRIENTS SUCH AS NITROGEN AND PHOSPHOROUS, WERE ONE REASON. OTHERS INCLUDED THE DISCHARGE OF UNTREATED SEWAGE AND RISING EMISSIONS FROM VEHICLES AND FACTORIES BEING ABSORBED BY THE OCEAN.

"DEAD ZONES WERE REGIONS WHERE THE WATER HAD UNUSUALLY LOW DISSOLVED OXYGEN CONTENT. ...WARMER WATERS, DUE TO CLIMATE CHANGE, COULD HOLD LESS DISSOLVED OXYGEN IN GENERAL...WARMER AIR WOULD HEAT UP THE SURFACE OF THE WATER, MAKING IT MORE BUOYANT AND REDUCING THE LIKIHOOD THAT THE TOP LAYERS WOULD MIX WITH THE COLDER WATER BELOW. ...WITHOUT MIXING, THE LOW-OXYGEN ZONE STICKS AROUND."[64]

WORLDWIDE, THERE WERE NOW WELL OVER 146 COASTAL DEAD ZONES. SINCE THE 1960'S, ACCORDING TO THE UNITED NATIONS GLOBAL ENVIRONMENT OUTLOOK, THE NUMBER OF DEAD ZONES HAD DOUBLED WITH EACH PASSING DECADE.

AND THEN THERE WAS THE ISSUE OF GARBAGE IN THE OCEANS. THE OCEANS STARTED TO LOOK LIKE TRASH PITS.

DISCARDED PLASTIC WAS ON COURSE TO OUTWEIGH FISH IN THE WORLD'S OCEANS BY 2050. "THE EIGHT MILLION TONS OF PLASTIC DUMPED INTO THE OCEAN EVERY YEAR WAS EQUAL TO FIVE GROCERY BAGS PER EVERY FOOT OF COASTLINE AROUND THE GLOBE.

SINCE 1964, GLOBAL PLASTIC PRODUCTION HAD INCREASED 20-FOLD...AND PRODUCTION WAS EXPECTED TO TRIPLE AGAIN BY 2050. ...THAT MEANT NOT ONLY MORE PLASTIC WASTE, BUT MORE PRODUCTION-RELATED OIL CONSUMPTION AND CARBON EMISSIONS..."[65]

THE PLANET WAS IN THE "...MIDST OF ITS SIXTH MASS EXTINCTION OF PLANTS AND ANIMALS," ACCORDING TO THE CENTER FOR BIOLOGICAL DIVERSITY. WE WERE "CURRENTLY EXPERIENCING THE WORST SPATE OF SPECIES DIE-OFF SINCE THE LOSS OF THE DINOSAURS 65 MILLION YEARS AGO. ALTHOUGH EXTINCTION IS A NATURAL PHENOMENON, IT OCCURS AS A NATURAL BACKGROUND RATE OF ABOUT ONE TO FIVE SPECIES PER YEAR. SCIENTISTS ESTIMATED WE WERE LOSING SPECIES AT 1,000 TO 10,000 TIMES THE BACKGROUND RATE."

HUMANS HAD DESTROYED HABITAT AND SPECIES AT AN ALARMING RATE.

IN 2013, EXOTIC ANIMAL TRADE WAS THE FIFTH LARGEST CONTRABAND TRADE, RANKING JUST BEHIND NARCOTICS. THE WORLD WILDLIFE FUND REPORTED THAT 52% OF THE WILDLIFE POPULATION AROUND THE WORLD HAD DISAPPEARED SINCE 1970.

FROM 2010 TO 2012 ALONE, APPROXIMATELY ONE FIFTH OF AFRICA'S ELEPHANT POPULATION -- ABOUT 100,000 -- WAS SLAUGHTERED BY POACHERS, ACCORDING TO SAVE THE ELEPHANTS.

"RHINO HORNS, WHICH ARE MADE OF KERATIN, LIKE YOUR FINGERNAILS, HAD LONG BEEN USED IN TRADITIONAL CHINESE MEDICINE BUT IN RECENT YEARS HAD BECOME EVEN MORE SOUGHT-AFTER AS A HIGH-END PARTY 'DRUG'; AT CLUBS IN SOUTHEAST ASIA, POWERED HORN WAS SNORTED LIKE COCAINE.

IN 2007, 13 RHINOS WERE POACHED IN SOUTH AFRICA; IN 2011 THE FIGURE SPIKED TO MORE THAN 1,000. RHINO HORN...(EVENTUALLY FETCHED ITS) WEIGHT IN GOLD -- ABOUT $30,000 PER POUND. IF THAT BUSINESS CONTINUED AS NORMAL, RHINOS WOULD BE EXTINCT BY 2020."[66]

AT ONE POINT IN 2016, 70% OF THE WORLD'S REMAINING FORESTS WERE WITHIN ONE KILOMETER OF A ROAD.[67] IMAGINE WHAT THAT MEANT FOR ANIMALS THAT ROAM, THAT NEEDED TO MIGRATE...IMAGINE THEIR VULNERABILITY TO HUMAN EXPLOITATION, AND THE IMPLICATIONS FOR DESTRUCTION OF HABITAT AND SPECIES IN GENERAL.

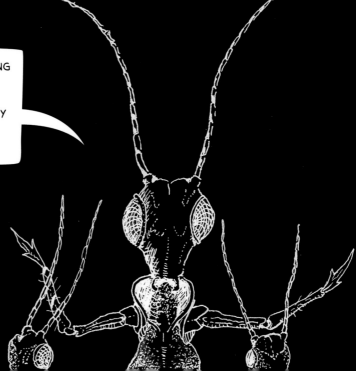

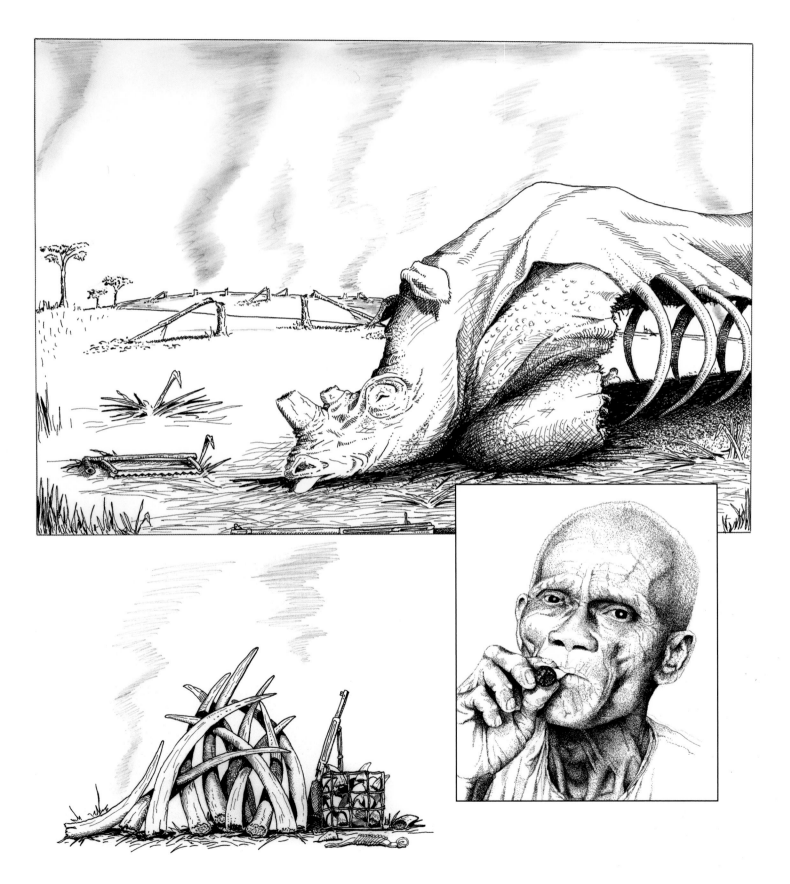

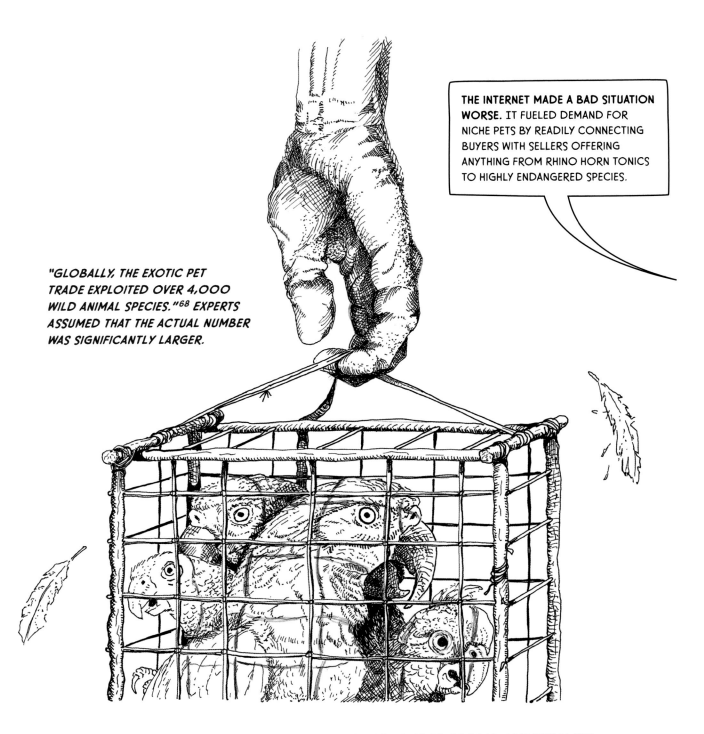

THE INTERNET MADE A BAD SITUATION WORSE. IT FUELED DEMAND FOR NICHE PETS BY READILY CONNECTING BUYERS WITH SELLERS OFFERING ANYTHING FROM RHINO HORN TONICS TO HIGHLY ENDANGERED SPECIES.

"GLOBALLY, THE EXOTIC PET TRADE EXPLOITED OVER 4,000 WILD ANIMAL SPECIES."[68] EXPERTS ASSUMED THAT THE ACTUAL NUMBER WAS SIGNIFICANTLY LARGER.

"THOUSANDS OF PARROTS WERE TAKEN FROM THE WILD EACH YEAR TO BE SOLD AS 'PETS' IN ASIA, EUROPE AND THE UNITED STATES. THE INITIAL SHOCK OF LOSING THEIR FREEDOM AND BEING CONFINED TO A CAGE WOULD KILL 10-20% OF WILD-CAUGHT BIRDS. OF THOSE WHO SURVIVED CAPTURE, HALF WOULD DIE OF STARVATION, DEHYDRATION, SUFFOCATION, OR DISEASE BEFORE REACHING THEIR FINAL DESTINATION. RESEARCHERS IN NICARAGUA ESTIMATED THAT, TO COMPENSATE FOR MORTALITIES, UP TO FOUR TIMES AS MANY PARROTS WERE CAPTURED THAN MAKE IT TO MARKET."[69]

THE TRENDS HUMANS CAUSED WERE CLEAR.

"BY THE END OF THE DECADE (2020), EARTH WAS FORECASTED TO...
LOSE 67% OF ALL VERTEBRATE WILDLIFE, COMPARED WITH LEVELS IN 1970"
ACCORDING TO THE LIVING PLANET REPORT.

"AND ORGANISMS LIVING IN FRESHWATER SYSTEMS SUCH AS RIVERS AND LAKES...
DECLINED 81% IN THE PAST FOUR DECADES...HABITAT LOSS AND OVEREXPLOITATION
WERE THE TWO BIGGEST THREATS..."[70]

AS IF THAT WASN'T ENOUGH, ACCORDING TO THE STATE OF WORLD'S PLANTS, IN
2016, ABOUT A FIFTH OF VASCULAR PLANTS (THINGS BOTANICAL THAT ARE NOT ALGAE,
MOSSES OR LIVERWORTS) WERE THREATENED WITH EXTINCTION. PLANTS, AND THE
PHOTOSYNTHESIS THAT POWERS THEM, REMAIN THE VERY STUFF OF HUMAN LIFE.[71]

"THE ONGOING MASS EXTINCTION OF SPECIES, AND WITH IT THE EXTINCTION OF GENES
AND ECOSYSTEMS, RANKED WITH PANDEMICS, WORLD WAR, AND CLIMATE CHANGE AS
AMONG THE DEADLIEST THREATS THAT HUMANITY HAD IMPOSED ON ITSELF."[72]

UNLIKE PAST EXTINCTIONS, CAUSED BY EVENTS
LIKE ASTEROID STRIKES, VOLCANIC ERUPTIONS
AND NATURAL CLIMATE SHIFTS, THIS EXTINCTION
WAS CAUSED ALMOST ENTIRELY BY HUMANS. IN
FACT, IN 2016, 99% OF THE THREATENED SPECIES
WERE AT RISK DUE TO HUMAN ACTIVITIES.[73]

THE WORLD HEALTH ORGANIZATION HAD CALLED CLIMATE CHANGE
THE GREATEST GLOBAL HEALTH THREAT OF THE 21ST CENTURY, AN
OPINION SHARED BY THE UNITED NATIONS, THE ENVIRONMENTAL PROTECTION
AGENCY AND THE NATIONAL INSTITUTE OF HEALTH. "...CLIMATE CHANGE WOULD
HAVE DEVASTATING CONSEQUENCES FOR HUMAN HEALTH FROM:

- CHANGING PATTERNS OF INFECTIONS AND INSECT BORNE DISEASES, AND
  INCREASED DEATHS DUE TO HEAT WAVES

- REDUCED WATER AND FOOD SECURITY, LEADING TO MALNUTRITION AND
  DIARRHEAL DISEASES

- INCREASE IN THE FREQUENCY AND MAGNITUDE OF EXTREME CLIMATE EVENTS
  (HURRICANES, CYCLONES, STORM SURGES) CAUSING FLOODING AND
  DIRECT INJURY

- INCREASED VULNERABILITY FOR THOSE LIVING IN URBAN SLUMS AND WHERE
  SHELTER AND HUMAN SETTLEMENTS WERE POOR

- LARGE-SCALE POPULATION MIGRATION AND THE LIKELIHOOD OF CIVIL UNREST"

NASA ASTRONAUTS ALSO "HELPED BUILD AWARENESS OF THE GROWING URGENCY OF CLIMATE CHANGE. ASTRONAUT SCOTT KELLY (WHO SPENT A YEAR IN SPACE)...SAID HE HAD SEEN CHANGES IN THE PLANET EVEN SINCE HIS PREVIOUS MISSION IN 2010. ...THERE IS MORE POLLUTION IN INDIA AND CHINA...WEATHER SYSTEMS WHERE THEY ARE NOT SUPPOSED TO BE OBVIOUS. THE FRAGILITY OF THE ATMOSPHERE ALWAYS APPARENT."[74]

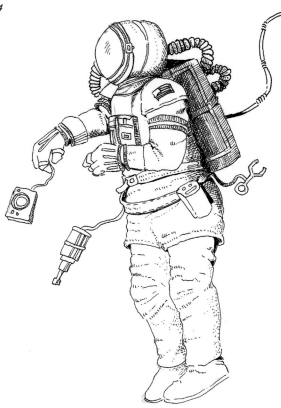

NASA...HAD BEEN CONSIDERING THE POSSIBLE EFFECTS OF CLIMATE CHANGE FOR NEARLY A DECADE. ...BY 2007, **"NASA HAD TO ACKNOWLEDGE CLIMATE CHANGE AND EXTREME WEATHER AS A FORMAL RISK"**[75]

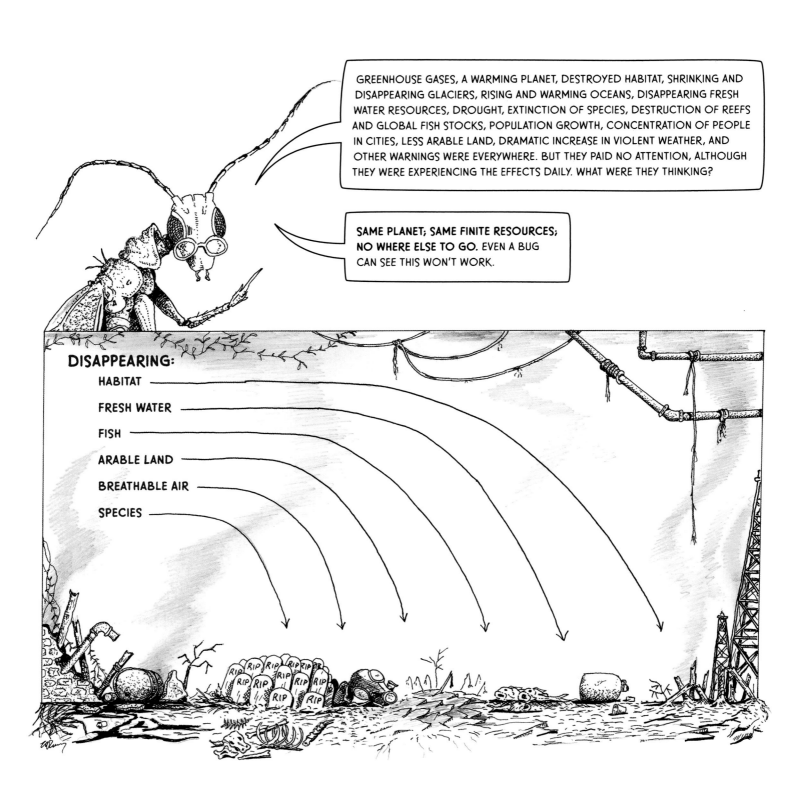

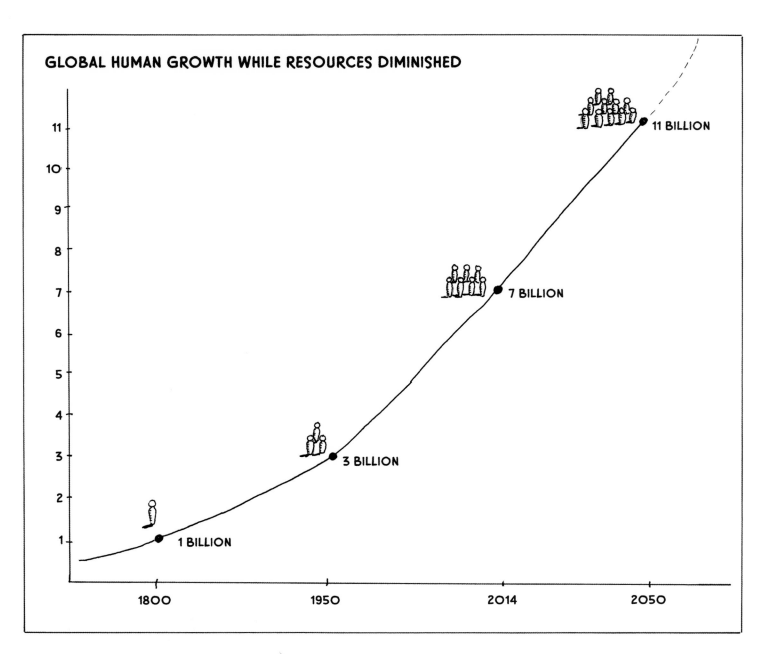

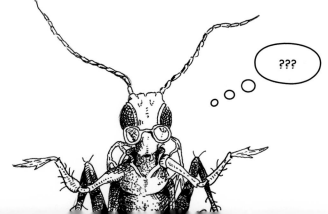

THERE WERE OTHER WARNINGS:

"AMONG THE FUTURE TRENDS THAT WILL IMPACT OUR NATIONAL SECURITY IS CLIMATE CHANGE. RISING GLOBAL TEMPERATURES, CHANGING PRECIPITATION PATTERNS, CLIMBING SEA LEVELS, AND MORE EXTREME WEATHER EVENTS WILL INTENSIFY THE CHALLENGES OF GLOBAL INSTABILITY, HUNGER, POVERTY, AND CONFLICT. THEY WILL LIKELY LEAD TO FOOD AND WATER SHORTAGES, PANDEMIC DISEASES, DISPUTES OVER REFUGEES AND RESOURCES, AND DESTRUCTION BY NATURAL DISASTERS IN REGIONS ACROSS THE GLOBE." CLIMATE CHANGE IS REFERRED TO AS A "THREAT MULTIPLIER."

-- POLICY STATEMENT,
U.S. DEPARTMENT OF DEFENSE, 2014

"ONCE CLIMATE CHANGE BECOMES A DEFINING ISSUE FOR FINANCIAL STABILITY, IT MAY ALREADY BE TOO LATE."

-- MARK CARNEY,
GOVERNOR OF THE BANK OF ENGLAND

"DOOMSDAY PREDICTIONS CAN NO LONGER BE MET WITH IRONY OR DISDAIN"
-- POPE FRANCIS

"BIODIVERSITY IS THE TOTALITY OF ALL INHERITED VARIATION IN THE LIFE FORMS OF EARTH, OF WHICH WE ARE ONE SPECIES. WE STUDY AND SAVE IT TO OUR GREAT BENEFIT. WE IGNORE AND DEGRADE IT TO OUR GREAT PERIL."
-- E. O. WILSON

"WATER AND AIR, THE TWO ESSENTIAL FLUIDS ON WHICH ALL LIFE DEPENDS, HAVE BECOME GLOBAL GARBAGE CANS."
-- JACQUES COUSTEAU

CHAPTER 3:

Insect Rodeo

IT'S TRUE THAT WE BITE, STING, SUCK BLOOD, AND CONSUME WOOD AND PLANTS. IT'S ALSO TRUE THAT **FOR 400 MILLION YEARS WE HAVE BEEN NURTURING THE PLANET, NOT DESTROYING IT.** HUMANS DECIDED, HOWEVER, THAT WE HAD TO GO, SO THEY TRIED TO TAME US. AFTER ALL, IF THEY COULD KILL US BY SIMPLY CRUSHING US BETWEEN TWO FINGERS, WHAT COULD BE SO DIFFICULT ABOUT ELIMINATING "PESTS"?

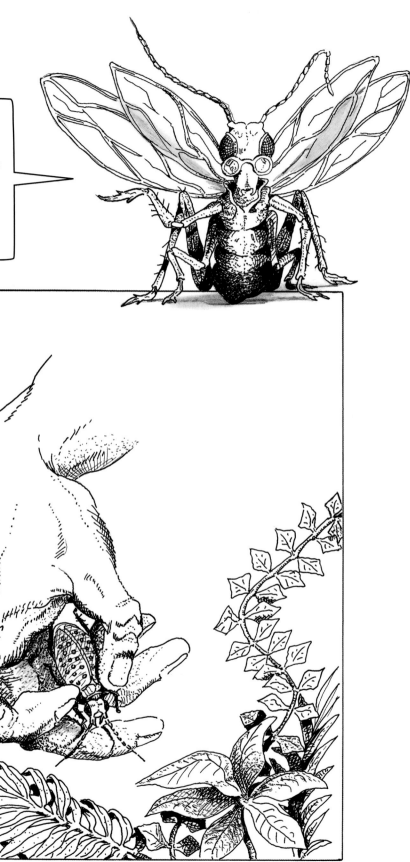

"...HUMAN ACTIONS WERE HASTENING PEST'S EVOLUTION OF RESISTANCE. FARMERS SPRAYED HIGH DOSES OF PESTICIDE IF THE TRADITIONAL DOSE DIDN'T KILL, SO GENETIC MECHANISMS THAT ENABLED THE PESTS TO SURVIVE THE STRONGER DOSES RAPIDLY BECAME WIDESPREAD AS THE OFF-SPRING OF RESISTANT INDIVIDUALS CAME TO DOMINATE THE POPULATION."[76]

UNPLEASANT AND DESTRUCTIVE. BUT INSECTS IN ALL THEIR VARIETY WERE COLLECTIVELY MORE BENEFICIAL THAN HARMFUL TO THE HUMAN WAY OF LIFE AND CERTAINLY **INDISPENSIBLE FOR THE LIFE AND HEALTH OF THE PLANET.**

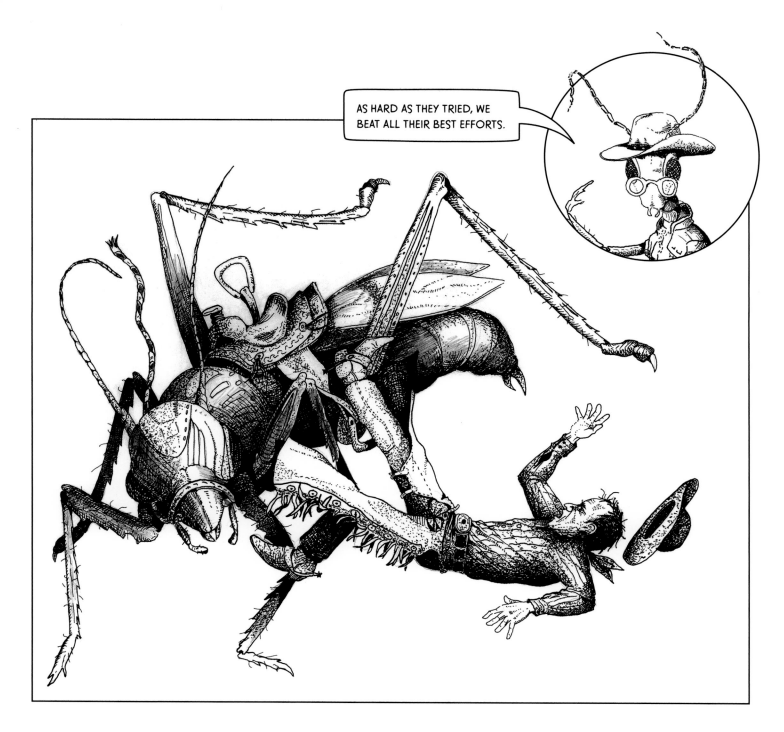

"HUNDREDS OF SPECIES OF HARMFUL INSECTS HAD ACQUIRED RESISTANCE TO DIFFERENT SYNTHETIC ORGANIC PESTICIDES, AND STRAINS THAT BECAME RESISTANT TO ONE INSECTICIDE COULD ALSO BE RESISTANT TO A SECOND THAT HAD A SIMILAR MODE OF ACTION TO THE FIRST...

THE NON-SPECIFIC NATURE OF BROAD-SPECTRUM CHEMICALS MADE THEM MORE LIKELY TO HAVE UNINTENDED EFFECTS ON THE ABUNDANCE OF BOTH HARMFUL AND BENEFICIAL INSECTS."[77]

"...DESPITE (HUMANS) BEST ATTEMPTS TO ERADICATE CERTAIN PEST SPECIES OVER THE PAST CENTURY, (THEY) HAD NOT EXTERMINATED A SINGLE ONE TO EXTINCTION."[78]

AND FOR ALL THEIR EFFORTS, WHAT HUMANS MANAGED TO DO WAS SEVERELY POLLUTE THEIR MOST PRECIOUS RESOURCE: WATER.

HUMANS DIRECTLY POISONING HUMANS IN AN ATTEMPT TO KILL US. RICH.

WHEN AN INSECTICIDE WAS APPLIED, MUCH OF IT REACHED THE SOIL, AND GROUNDWATER WAS ALSO CONTAMINATED. WITH REPEATED SPRAYINGS, THESE CHEMICALS ACCUMULATED IN SOILS IN SURPRISINGLY LARGE AMOUNTS. THEIR EFFECT ON WILDLIFE WAS GREATLY INCREASED AS THEY BECAME ASSOCIATED WITH THE FOOD CHAINS.[79]

THE UNITED STATES GEOLOGICAL SURVEY (USGS) FOUND "THAT MORE THAN 90% OF WATER AND FISH SAMPLES FROM ALL STREAMS SAMPLED IN THE U.S. CONTAINED AT LEAST ONE PESTICIDE. WELL WATER IS DRAWN FROM GROUND WATER SOURCES...USGS FOUND THAT AROUND 50% OF WELL SAMPLES CONTAINED ONE OR MORE PESTICIDES."

THE EPA SAID BY THEIR VERY NATURE, MOST PESTICIDES CREATED SOME RISK TO HUMANS, ANIMALS, OR ENVIRONMENT BECAUSE THEY ARE DESIGNED TO KILL OR OTHERWISE ADVERSELY AFFECT LIVING ORGANISMS.

"STUDIES OF MAJOR RIVERS AND STREAMS DOCUMENTED THAT 96% OF ALL FISH, 100% OF ALL WATER SAMPLES AND 33% OF MAJOR AQUIFERS CONTAINED ONE OR MORE PESTICIDES AT DETECTABLE LEVELS."[80]

CHAPTER 4:

The Fatal Flaw

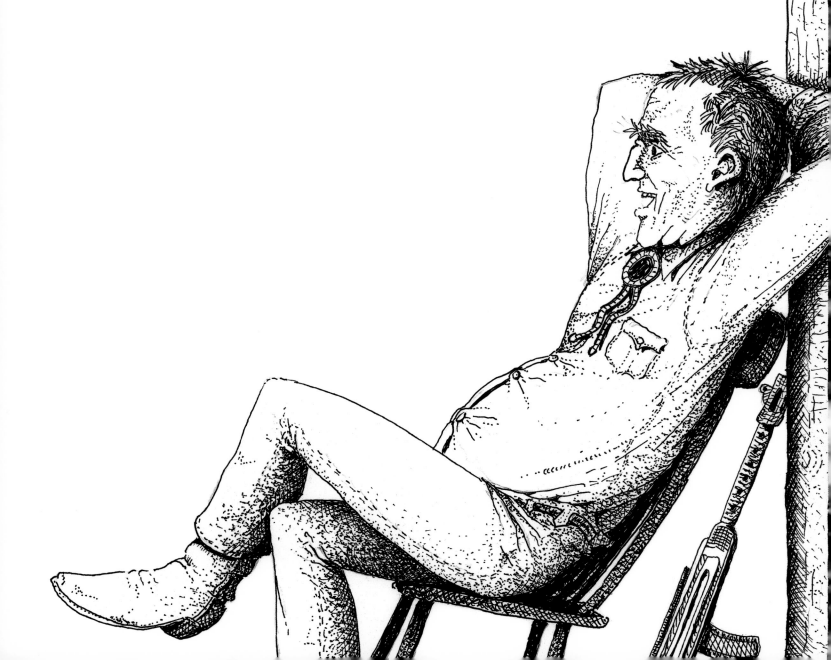

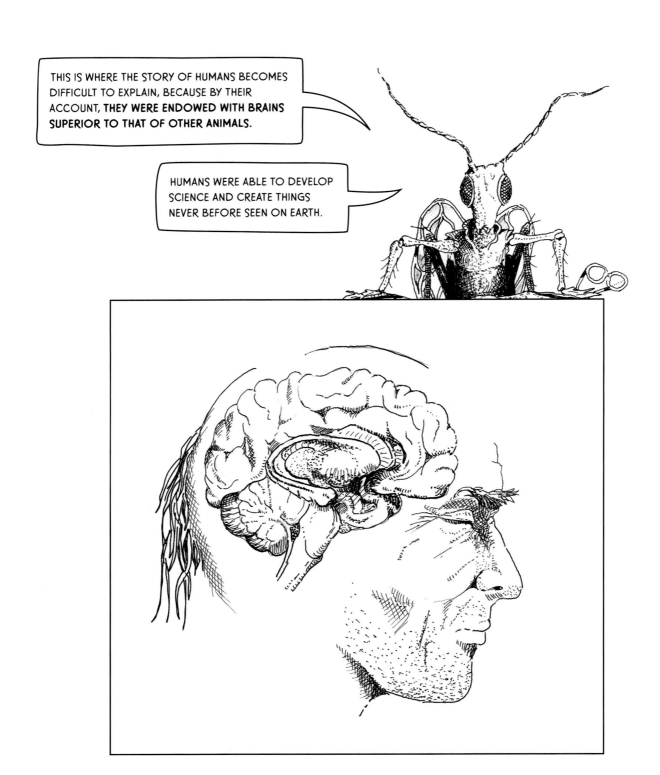

THIS IS WHERE THE STORY OF HUMANS BECOMES DIFFICULT TO EXPLAIN, BECAUSE BY THEIR ACCOUNT, **THEY WERE ENDOWED WITH BRAINS SUPERIOR TO THAT OF OTHER ANIMALS.**

HUMANS WERE ABLE TO DEVELOP SCIENCE AND CREATE THINGS NEVER BEFORE SEEN ON EARTH.

*LARGE BRAINS ALLOWED HUMANS "TO PROCESS AND STORE INFORMATION, TO PLAN AHEAD. **THEY WERE CAPABLE OF SELF-RESTRAINT, AND CHOICES."** [81]*

"THEY LEARNED HOW TO EXPLOIT FOSSIL FUELS AND HOW TO CLEAR LAND IN UNPRECEDENTED WAYS, CHANGING LANDSCAPES INSTANTLY. THEY DEVELOPED AN INDUSTRIAL PROCESS FOR CREATING FERTILIZER, BREAKING CONSTRAINTS ON FOOD PRODUCTION. SANITATION SYSTEMS WERE DEVELOPED, ALONG WITH MAJOR MEDICAL ADVANCES, RESULTING IN GREAT BENEFITS FOR HUMAN HEALTH AND FOSTERING THE GROWTH OF URBAN ENVIRONMENTS. POPULATION GREW, AS DID LIFE EXPECTANCY."[82] THE LIST OF SCIENTIFIC ACHIEVEMENTS GREW EXPONENTIALLY, MOSTLY FOR THE BETTER.

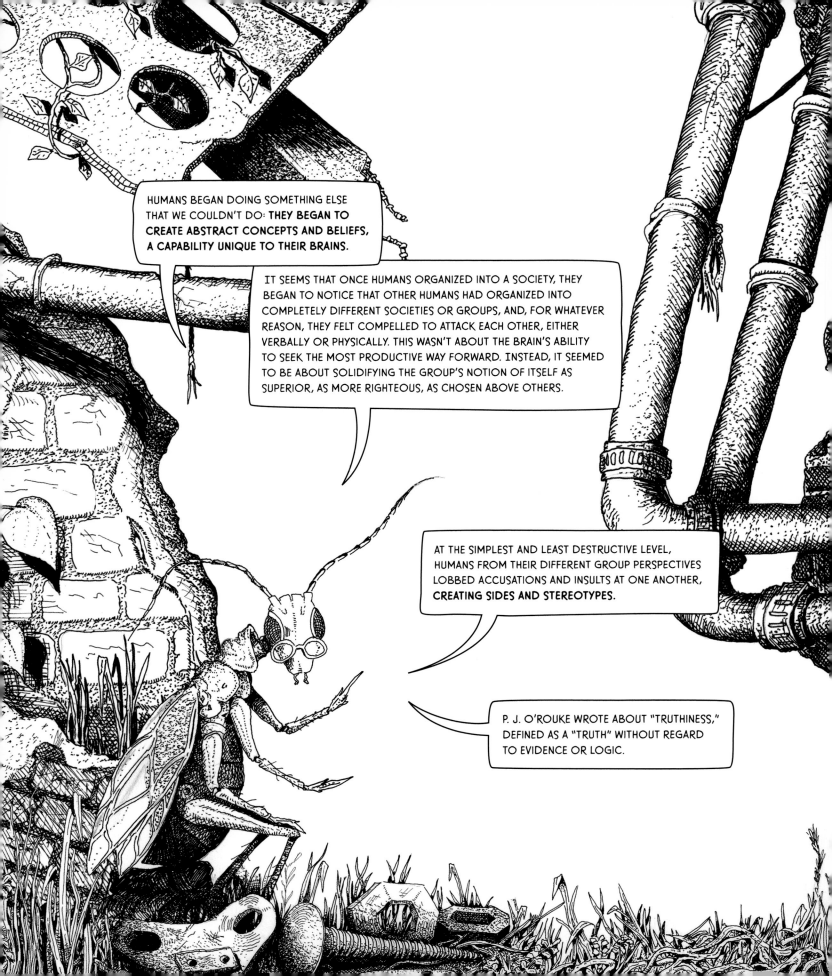

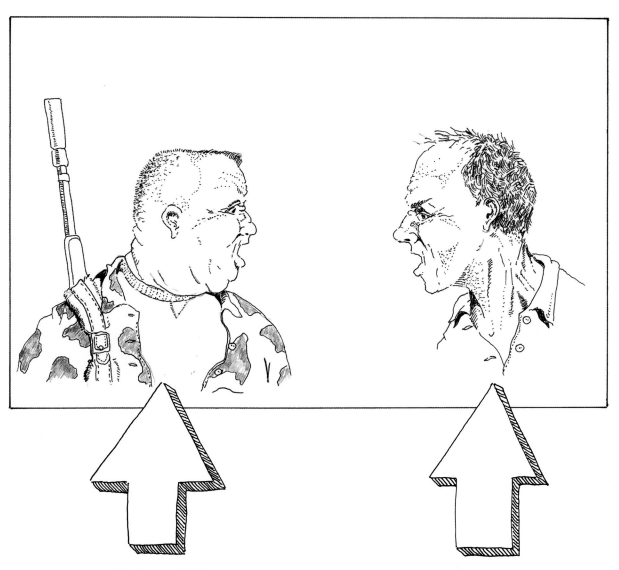

CONSERVATIVE WERE "THOSE HATEFUL, ASSAULT-WEAPON-WIELDING MANIACS WHO BELIEVE THAT GEORGE WASHINGTON AND JESUS CHRIST INCORPORATED THE NATION AFTER A GETTYSBURG REENACTMENT AND THAT THE ONLY THING WRONG WITH THE DEATH PENALTY WAS THAT IT WASN'T ADMINISTERED QUICKLY ENOUGH TO SECULAR-HUMANIST PROFESSORS OF CHICANO STUDIES"*

LIBERALS WERE "PINKO-COMMUNIST FLAG BURNERS WHO WANTED TO TAX CHURCHES AND USE THE MONEY TO FUND ABORTIONS SO THEY COULD USE THE FETAL STEM CELLS TO CREATE POT-SMOKING LESBIAN ATF AGENTS WHO WOULD STEAL ALL THE GUNS AND INVITE THE UNITED NATIONS TO TAKE OVER AMERICA."*

*P. J. O'ROUKE

ACCUSATIONS BASED ON BELIEFS LEVELED AT ONE GROUP OR ANOTHER WAS ONE THING. BUT DENYING THE ACQUIRED KNOWLEDGE, THE BY-PRODUCT OF THEIR OWN UNIQUE CAPACITY FOR SCIENTIFIC AND REASONED INQUIRY, WAS MYSTIFYING.

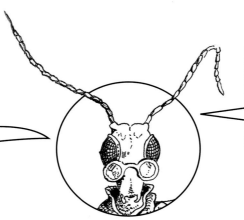

IT WAS THE PARALLEL CAPACITY OF THE BRAIN TO COMMIT TO A BELIEF, EVEN WHEN EVIDENCE INDICATED OTHERWISE, THAT THE REST OF US STILL DON'T UNDERSTAND. HOW COULD THEY DO THAT? THEY HAD AN EXTRAORDINARY GIFT AND CANCELLED OUT ITS ADVANTAGE.

MARK TWIN SAID "IT AIN'T WHAT YOU DON'T KNOW THAT GETS YOU IN TROUBLE. IT'S WHAT YOU KNOW FOR SURE THAT JUST AIN'T SO."

TOM DONOHUE, PRESIDENT OF THE U.S. CHAMBER OF COMMERCE, SAID "THERE IS NO WAY THIS (CUTTING BACK ON USE OF FOSSIL FUELS) CAN BE DONE WITHOUT FUNDAMENTALLY CHANGING THE AMERICAN WAY OF LIFE... AND PUTTING LARGE SEGMENTS OF OUR ECONOMY OUT OF BUSINESS."

THE REAL ISSUE FOR THE FOSSIL FUEL INDUSTRY WAS "SCIENTISTS ESTIMATED THAT (THEIR) INDUSTRY OWNED ROUGHLY FIVE TIMES MORE OIL, GAS, AND COAL THAN THE PLANET COULD SAFELY BURN. ...80% OF THE INDUSTRY'S RESERVES WOULD HAVE TO STAY IN THE GROUND."[83]

THE LATE MINISTER JERRY FALWELL, FOUNDER OF LIBERTY UNIVERSITY: "I CAN TELL YOU, OUR GRAND-CHILDREN WILL LAUGH AT THOSE WHO PREDICTED GLOBAL WARMING. WE'LL BE IN GLOBAL COOLING

O. WILSON: "DEEMING OURSELVES RULERS OF THE BIOSPHERE AND ITS SUPREME ACHIEVEMENT WE BELIEVED URSELVES ENTITLED TO DO ANYTHING TO THE REST OF LIFE WE WISHED."

ONCE A GROUP HAS BEEN SPLIT OFF AND SUFFICIENTLY DEHUMANIZED ANY BRUTALITY CAN BE JUSTIFIED, " ANY LEVEL, AND AT ANY SIZE OF THE VICTIMIZED GROUP UP TO AND INCLUDING RACE AND NATIONS."[84]

HEMICAL WEAPONS WERE CLASSIFIED AS WEAPONS OF MASS DESTRUCTION. "THEY BECOME WEAPONS WHEN EY ARE PLACED INTO ARTILLERY SHELLS, LAND MINES, AERIAL BOMBS, MISSILE WARHEADS, MORTAR SHELLS, RENADES, SPRAY TANKS, OR ANY OTHER MEANS OF DELIVERING THE AGENTS TO DESIGNATED TARGETS."[85]

HUMANS WERE THE ONLY SPECIES THAT KILLED OTHER MEMBERS OF THEIR OWN SPECIES BECAUSE OF DIFFERENCES IN BELIEFS, OR CULTURE. THEY WERE THE ONLY SPECIES THAT BUILT AND USED WEAPONS TO DESTROY EACH OTHER. THEY WERE THE ONLY SPECIES TO TORTURE. HUMANS DEVELOPED THE CAPACITY AND STOCKPILES TO EXTINGUISH THEMSELVES AND THE EARTH SEVERAL TIMES OVER. IT WAS ACCEPTABLE TO USE SCIENCE FOR ARMED DESTRUCTION, BUT NOT FOR RECOGNIZING OR FIGHTING CATASTROPHIC CLIMATE CHANGE OR PROTECTING BIODIVERSITY.

WHILE ALL OF THIS WAS EVOLVING, WE WERE IN THE DARK CREVICES OF THEIR BUILDINGS, LABORATORIES, AND MILITARY BASES, THRIVING AS WE HAD FOR MILLIONS OF YEARS.

WHY DID HUMANS MOVE WITH SUCH DELIBERATION TO DESTROY ONE ANOTHER WITH NO OBVIOUS PRACTICAL BENEFIT?

ZBIGNEW BRZEZINSKI, FORMER NATIONAL SECURITY ADVISOR, WROTE THAT THOSE KILLED IN 20TH CENTURY WARS TOTALED "87,000,000 LIVES WITH THE NUMBER OF WOUNDED, MAIMED, OR OTHERWISE AFFLICTED BEYOND ESTIMATE. THESE STAGGERING NUMBERS ARE MATCHED...BY A MORE HORRIFYING TOTAL: 175,000,000 WERE DELIBERATELY EXTINGUISHED THROUGH POLITICALLY MOTIVATED CARNAGE. THESE WERE DEFENSELESS INDIVIDUALS DELIBERATELY PUT TO DEATH BECAUSE OF DOCTRINAL HATRED AND PASSIONS. THESE HORRENDOUS... NUMBERS ARE...WHAT CAN HAPPEN WHEN HUMANITY'S INNATE CAPACITY FOR AGGRESSION BECOMES HARNESSED BY DOGMATIC SELF-RIGHTEOUSNESS AND IS ENHANCED BY INCREASINGLY POTENT TECHNOLOGIES OF DESTRUCTION."[86]

THE IPCC (INTERGOVERNMENTAL PANEL ON CLIMATE CHANGE): "VIOLENT CONFLICT INCREASED VULNERABILITY TO CLIMATE CHANGE. LARGE SCALE CONFLICT HARMED ASSETS THAT FACILITATE ADAPTATION, INCLUDING INFRASTRUCTURE, INSTITUTIONS, NATURAL RESOURCES, SOCIAL CAPITAL, AND LIVELIHOOD OPPORTUNITIES."

"MORE PEOPLE WERE ON THE RUN (IN 2015) THAN EVER BEFORE IN RECORDED HISTORY, ACCORDING TO THE UNITED NATIONS REFUGEE AGENCY. THE NUMBER OF PEOPLE DISPLACED BY CONFLICT WAS ESTIMATED TO EXCEED 65 MILLION. THEY WERE FLEEING WAR, PERSECUTION, POVERTY OR ENVIRONMENTAL DEVASTATION. THAT FIGURE EXCLUDED PEOPLE DISPLACED BY EARTHQUAKES, FLOODS AND OTHER NATURAL DISASTERS, WHICH IN 2015 UP-ROOTED AT LEAST 19 MILLION."[87]

CLIMATE CHANGE WAS POISED TO HELP CREATE THE MOST DANGEROUS PLACES ON EARTH: FAILED STATES. FAILED BECAUSE OF DROUGHT, FAMINE, DISEASE, PESTILENCE, INABILITY TO RESPOND TO HISTORIC NATURAL CATASTROPHES, RISE IN SEA LEVEL, LACK OF FRESH WATER, AND EXTRA-TERRITORIAL AGGRESSION AND BRUTALITY USED TO JUSTIFY POWER.

GENERAL DWIGHT EISENHOWER, SUPREME ALLIED COMMANDER IN WORLD WAR II, LEADER OF THE D DAY INVASION AND 34TH PRESIDENT OF THE UNITED STATES: "WAR IS MANKIND'S MOST TRAGIC AND STUPID FOLLY..."

"MILITANT ENTHUSIASM CAN BE STIMULATED BY THE PRESENCE OF A HATED
ENEMY WHO THREATENS VALUES. THIS ENEMY CAN BE OF A CONCRETE OR ABSTRACT
NATURE. IT CAN BE 'THE' JEWS, HUNS, (MUSLIMS), CHRISTIANS, TYRANTS...OR ABSTRACT
CONCEPTS LIKE CAPITALISM, COMMUNISM, FASCISM, AND ANY OTHER KIND OF ISM; IT CAN
BE HERESY, DOGMATISM, SCIENTIFIC FALLACY...JUST AS IN THE CASE OF THE OBJECT TO BE
DEFENDED, THE ENEMY AGAINST WHO TO DEFEND IT IS EXTREMELY VARIABLE."[88]

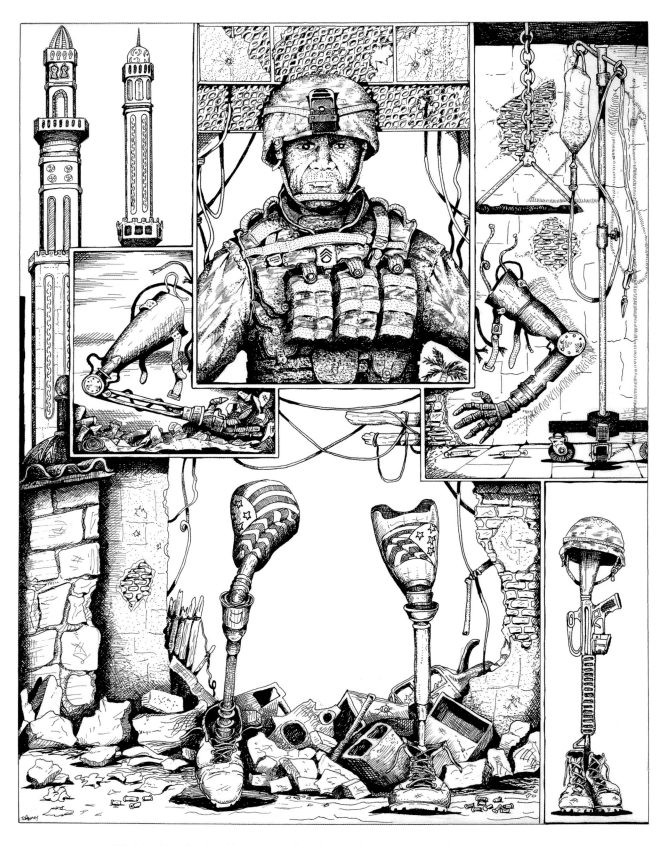

DWIGHT EISENHOWER: *"I BELIEVE THAT WAR IS THE DEADLY HARVEST OF ARROGANT AND UNREASONING MINDS."*

COLLATERAL DAMAGE

SURVIVOR, THE SEED OF VENGEANCE; INTENSE, CRUEL, AND INSATIABLE

WHATEVER THE EMOTIONAL TRIGGERS, WHETHER "THEY ARE -- VALUES, IDEALS, ANCESTORS, FATHER, MOTHER, THE SOIL, COUNTRY, CLASS, RELIGION, AND HUNDREDS OF OTHER PHENOMENA -- THEY ARE PERCEIVED AS SACRED. THE INDIVIDUAL -- OR GROUP -- REACTS TO AN ATTACK AGAINST THE 'SACRED' WITH THE SAME RAGE AND AGGRESSIVENESS AS TO AN ATTACK AGAINST LIFE." THIS FUELS A CYCLE OF RETALIATORY VIOLENCE WHICH CAN LAST FOR GENERATIONS.[89]

WE INSECTS DO NOT ENJOY INFLICTING SUFFERING ON OTHER ANIMALS, NOR DO WE KILL WITHOUT REASON. FOR HUMANS, SUBJUGATION AND DOMINANCE ALWAYS SEEMED TO SET THE TABLE FOR THE NEXT HORRIFIC CONFLICT.

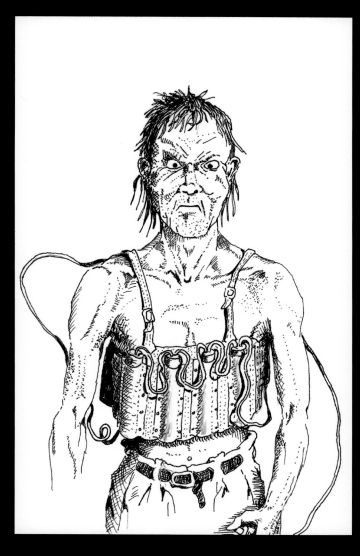

"THE INSTINCTIVE NEED TO BE A MEMBER OF A CLOSELY KNIT GROUP FIGHTING FOR COMMON IDEALS MAY GROW SO STRONG THAT IT BECOMES INESSENTIAL WHAT THOSE IDEALS ARE AND WHETHER THEY POSSESS ANY INTRINSIC VALUE." [91]

"...FOR MOST PEOPLE REALITY IS CONSTITUTED BY GENERAL CONSENSUS AND NOT BASED ON REASON OR CRITICAL EXAMINATION." [92]

OR, THE BOMB COULD HAVE BEEN IN A TERRORIST CONTAMINATED SHIP.

OR, A MID-RANGE OR INTERCONTINENTAL BALLISTIC MISSILE COULD HAVE BEEN LAUNCHED. VIOLATING AND UNDERMINING ARMS CONTROL TREATIES HAD BECOME THE NORM.

AN ENTIRE CITY INSTANTLY BECAME UNINHABITABLE. EVERYTHING WAS CONTAMINATED. PANIC, TERROR, AND RAGE ENVELOPED MILLIONS OF PEOPLE, THE ENTIRETY OF A NATION, AND NATIONS. **THE BRIDGE TO THE UNTHINKABLE HAD BEEN CROSSED.**

"A 10 TO 20 KILOTON WEAPON DETONATED IN A MAJOR SEAPORT WOULD KILL 50,000 TO 1 MILLION PEOPLE...CONTAINERS COULD EASILY HOLD A NUCLEAR WEAPON...(PLAUSIBLE) SOURCES FOR SUCH A BOMB...RUSSIA...PAKISTAN..."[93] OR NORTH KOREA.

NOTE: THE COMPREHENSIVE NUCLEAR TEST BAN TREATY OF 1996 (CTBT) WAS NEVER RATIFIED BY CHINA, EGYPT, INDIA, PAKISTAN, ISRAEL, NORTH KOREA, OR THE UNITED STATES.

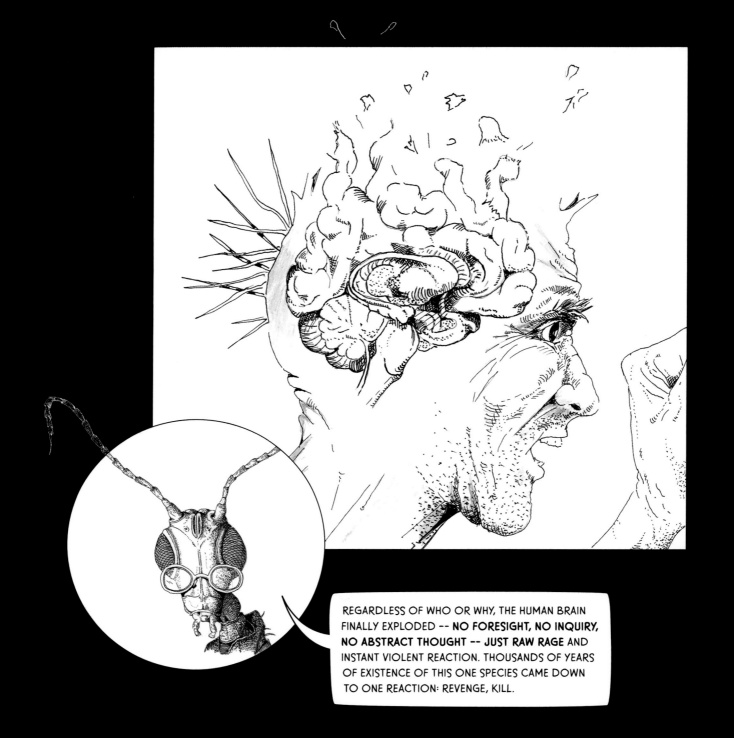

BEFORE THE EXPLOSION OF THE BOMB THOUGH, **SEVERAL THINGS HAD HAPPENED TO ASSURE THE INEVITABILITY OF THE RESPONSE:**

ONE, WAS THAT WITH PEOPLE, "LOCKED INSIDE THEIR RESPECTIVE ECHO CHAMBERS, PARTICULARLY ON SOCIAL MEDIA, USUALLY EVEN HANDED COMMENTATORS, THEY ALL LOST THEIR BEARINGS. STRAW MEN BESTRODE THE LANDSCAPE, AND PARANOIA AND CONSPIRACY THEORIES FLOURISHED." [94]

ANOTHER, WAS THAT THE UNITED STATE, RUSSIA AND CHINA WERE "AGGRESSIVELY PURSUING A NEW GENERATION OF...NUCLEAR WEAPONS. THE BUILD UPS THREATENED TO REVIVE A COLD WAR-ERA ARMS RACE AND UNSETTLE THE BALANCE OF DESTRUCTIVE FORCE AMONG NATIONS THAT (HAD) KEPT THE NUCLEAR PEACE FOR MORE THAN A HALF-CENTURY. ...THE LEVEL OF UNCERTAINLY, THE VELOCITY OF INSTABILITY, AND THE SIGNIFICANT INTER-STATE CONFLICT (WAS) HIGHER THAN IT HAS BEEN SINCE THE COLD WAR." [95]

ALSO, INSTABILITY WAS DRIVEN BY DIMINISHING RESOURCES, POPULATION OUTGROWING AND DESTROYING THE FINITE CAPACITY OF THE PLANET, AND ENDLESS TERRORISM AND ARMED CONFLICT FROM ALL CORNERS OF THE PLANET. AND INSTRUCTIONS FOR BUILDING DIRTY AND REGULAR NUCLEAR WEAPONS ON THE INTERNET.

AND THEN, THERE WERE THE ROGUE CRAZIES THAT WERE EVERYWHERE.

AFTER THE BOMB WENT OFF, PANIC GRIPPED THE WORLD, AND SOME COUNTRY OR COUNTRIES, **SEEKING REVENGE, OR FEARING RETALIATION, OR DRIVEN BY THEIR OWN CONSPIRACY THEORIES, OR PARANOIA,** PUSHED THE NUCLEAR BUTTON. **NO ONE WANTED TO BE THE LAST TO BE DESTROYED.**

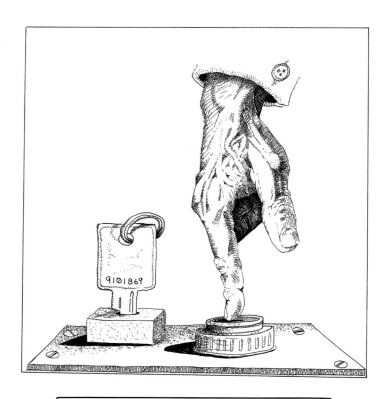

WAS IT A "RESPONSIBLE" NATION THAT FIRED FIRST?

OR, WAS IT AN "IRRESPONSIBLE" NATION?

IT MAKES NO DIFFERENCE: SOMEONE HIT THE BUTTON. THE YEAR WAS 2150.

THE NATIONAL CENTER FOR ATMOSPHERIC RESEARCH: "...IT WOULDN'T TAKE A FULL SCALE NUCLEAR WAR, LIKE A CONFLICT BETWEEN INDIA AND PAKISTAN, TO MAKE THE EARTH UNINHABITABLE. ...A VERY SMALL REGIONAL NUCLEAR WAR ON THE OTHER SIDE OF THE PLANET COULD DISRUPT GLOBAL CLIMATE FOR AT LEAST A DECADE AND WIPE OUT THE OZONE LAYER." *IT WOULD BE CATASTROPHIC GIVEN THE FRAGILE AND DETERIORATING STATE OF THE ENVIRONMENT.*

IN 2017 THERE WERE MORE THAN 15,500 NUCLEAR WARHEADS ON THE PLANET. ENOUGH TO BLOW UP THE PLANET AT LEAST THREE TIMES. ONE HUNDRED AND THIRTY-THREE YEARS LATER, THERE WERE TWICE THAT AMOUNT. EVERYONE KNEW HOW TO BUILD THEM, EVERYONE WANTED THEM, FELT THEY NEEDED THEM. EVEN IF SOME HUMANS MANAGED TO SURVIVE, THEY HAD RENDERED THE PLANET UNSALVAGEABLE.

BIODIVERSITY TO SUSTAIN LIFE WAS BELOW THE TIPPING POINT OF SURVIVAL; 60% OF THE CREATURES THAT EXISTED IN 2017 WERE NOW EXTINCT. DISEASE, PESTILENCE, AND FAMINE WERE GRIPPING THE EARTH AS A RESULT OF SUSTAINED CHANGES IN WEATHER PATTERNS; FRESH WATER, THE MOST PRECIOUS COMMODITY ON EARTH WAS DISAPPEARING; FISH HAD VANISHED FROM THE OCEAN; MAJOR COASTAL URBAN CENTERS WERE UNDERWATER; CIVILIZATIONS' **SOCIAL VALUES HAD DISAPPEARED AS EVERYONE STRUGGLED TO SURVIVE AND BLAMED OTHERS FOR THEIR PLIGHT.**

THERE WASN'T EVEN TIME TO CALL IT WORLD WAR III, IT WAS OVER THAT FAST.

ALBERT EINSTEIN: "THE UNLEASHED POWER OF THE ATOM HAS CHANGED EVERYTHING SAVE OUR MODE OF THINKING AND WE THUS DRIFT TOWARD UNPARALLELED CATASTROPHE."

CHAPTER 5:

The Junk Yard

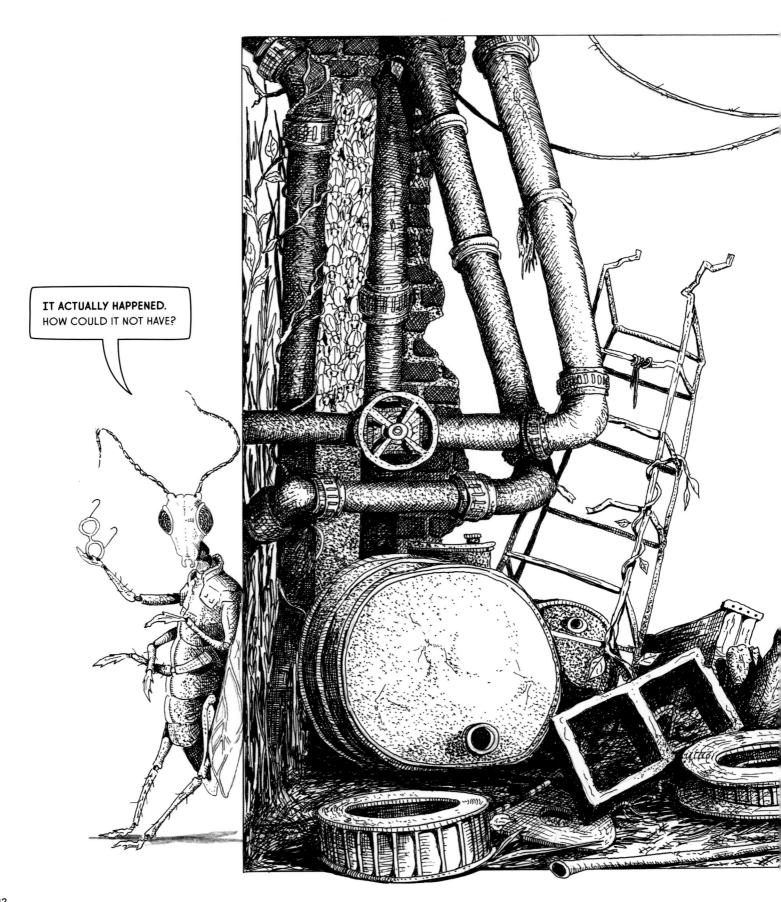

"IT IS ONLY WHEN WE THINK ABSTRACTLY," SAID BERTRAND RUSSELL,
"THAT WE HAVE SUCH A HIGH OPINION OF MAN."

THE FEW EMACIATED HUMANS LEFT FOUGHT TO THE DEATH OVER BOTTLES OF WATER AND THE FEW EDIBLE PRE-PACKAGED FOODS REMAINING ON EARTH. NOTHING COULD GROW, ALL WATER WAS CONTAMINATED, NO ANIMALS WERE ALIVE TO BE HUNTED.

THE U.S. ARMY SURVIVAL MANUAL OUTLINED THE SURVIVAL
RULES OF THREE -- **AIR, SHELTER, WATER, FOOD:**

- YOU CAN SURVIVE FOR <u>3 MINUTES WITHOUT AIR</u>

- YOU CAN SURVIVE FOR <u>3 HOURS WITHOUT SHELTER</u>
  IN A HARSH ENVIRONMENT (FREEZING COLD)

- YOU CAN SURVIVE FOR <u>3 DAYS WITHOUT WATER</u>

- YOU CAN SURVIVE FOR <u>3 WEEKS WITHOUT FOOD</u>
  (IF YOU HAVE WATER AND SHELTER)

WHILE THE FEW HUMAN SURVIVORS WERE KILLING ONE ANOTHER FOR THE LAST MORSELS OF FOOD AND DROPS OF WATER, WE WERE SORTING THROUGH ALL **THE DETRITUS, THE JUNK,** TO FIND WHAT WE COULD RECYCLE AND REBUILD.

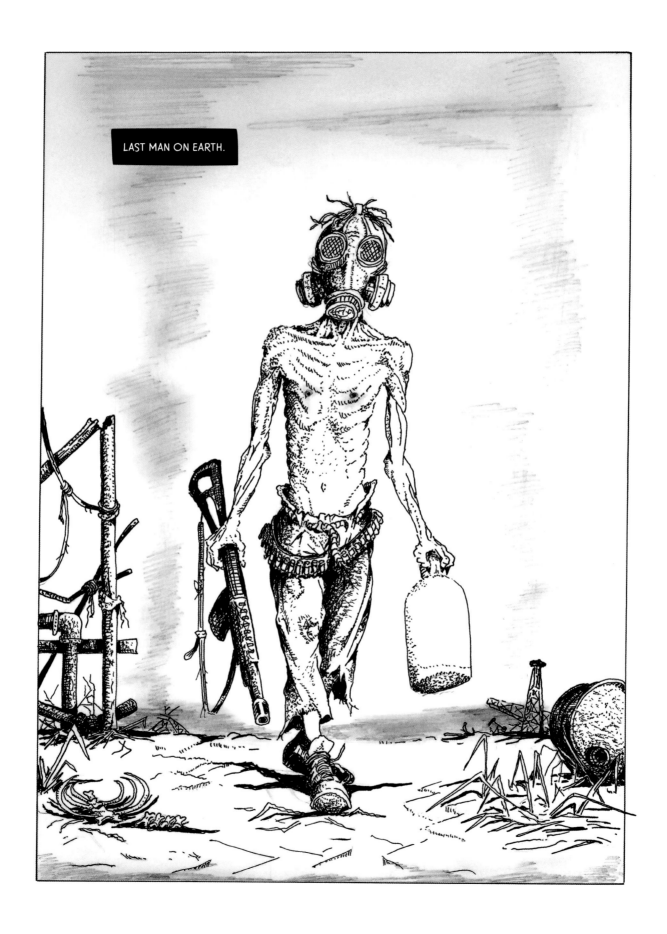

SEPTEMBER 15, 2150, THE LAST DAY, THE LAST MOMENT OF THE LAST MAN ON EARTH.

EPILOGUE

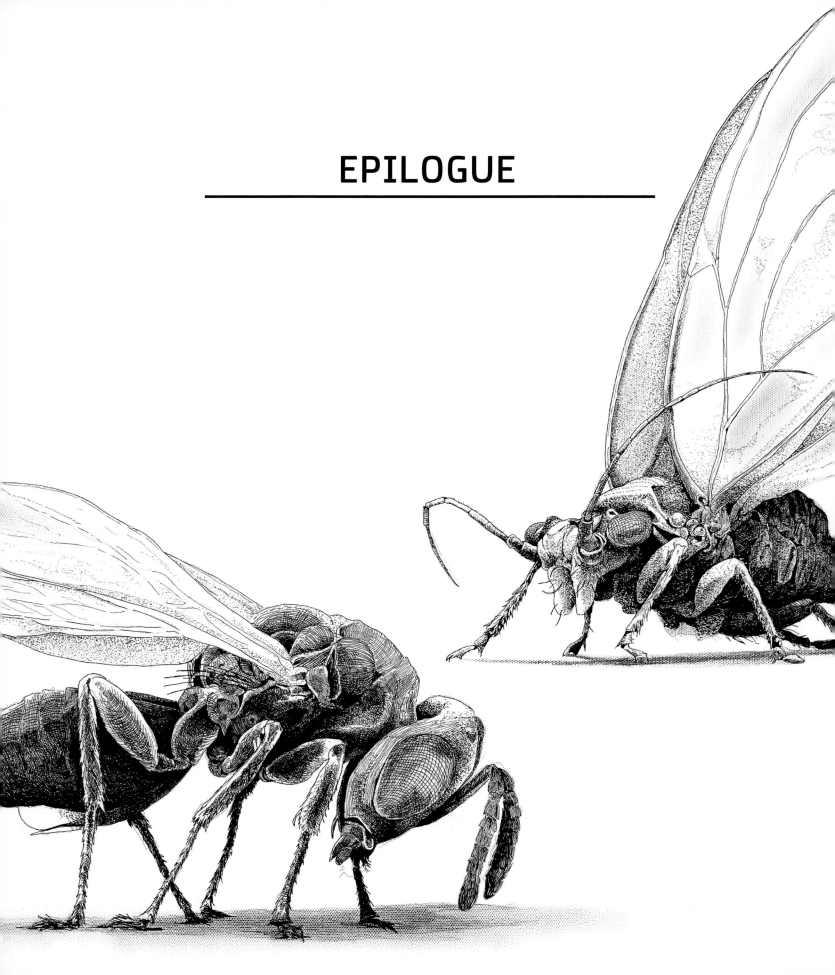

...AND DOGS.

SAM

BERKELEY

* THE PARIS AGREEMENT ON CLIMATE CHANGE WAS ENACTED ON NOVEMBER 4, 2016. IT, FOR THE FIRST TIME, BROUGHT "ALL NATIONS INTO COMMON CAUSE TO UNDERTAKE AMBITIOUS EFFORTS TO COMBAT CLIMATE CHANGE AND ADAPT TO ITS EFFECTS, WITH ENHANCED SUPPORT TO ASSIST DEVELOPING COUNTRIES."

-- UNFCCC (UNITED NATIONS FRAMEWORK CONVENTION ON CLIMATE CHANGE), UNFCCC.INT

** RENEWABLE ENERGY RESOURCES COULD HAVE EXPONENTIALLY EXCEEDED THE WORLD'S ENERGY DEMANDS AND NOT CONTRIBUTED TO GREENHOUSE EMISSIONS. RESEARCH AND DEVELOPMENT AND INVESTMENTS WERE NEEDED.

RECOMMENDED READING
which offers hope and action to be taken:

THE AGE OF SUSTAINABLE DEVELOPMENT
BY JEFFREY D. SACKS

CLIMATE CHANGE: WHAT EVERYONE NEEDS TO KNOW
BY JOSEPH ROMM

EARTH: MAKING A LIFE ON A TOUGH NEW PLANET
BY BILL MCKIBBEN

DIRE PREDICTIONS: UNDERSTANDING CLIMATE CHANGE
BY MICHAEL E. MANN AND LEE R. KUMP

RECOMMENDED WEB SITES

350.ORG	350.ORG
ENVIRONMENTAL DEFENSE FUND	EDF.ORG
FRIENDS OF THE EARTH	FOE.ORG
INTERNATIONAL FUND FOR ANIMAL WELFARE	IFAW.ORG
NATURAL RESOURCES DEFENSE COUNCIL	NRDC.ORG
NATURE CONSERVANCY	NATURE.ORG
THE SIERRA CLUB	SIERRACLUB.ORG
WORLD WILDLIFE FUND	WORLDWILDLIFE.ORG
XERCES SOCIETY	XERCES.ORG

PAY ATTENTION TO LOCAL AND NATIONAL POLITICS.

VOTE, ACT AND CONTRIBUTE!

ENDNOTES

1. Dunham, Will, "What Were The First Bugs Like?" *The Christian Science Monitor,* c+s+monitor.com/science/2014/1107, November 7, 2014

2. Walters, Martin, *The Illustrated World Encyclopedia of Insects,* Lorenz Books, London, 2014, p. 11

3. Shaw, Scott Richard, *Planet of Bugs,* University of Chicago Press, Chicago, 2014, p. 85

4. Honovich, Nancy; Murawski, Darlyne, *The Ultimate Bugopedia,* National Geographic, Washington, DC, 2013, p.62

5. Walters, Martins, *The Illustrated World Encyclopedia of Insects,* Lorenz Books, London, 2014, p. 12

6. "Anthropods: Creatures That Rule" (Museum exhibit, 2016), Harvard Museum of Natural History, Harvard University, Cambridge.

7. Fleming, Nic, "Which Life Form Dominates Earth," www.bbc.com/earth/story/20150211-whats-the-most-dominant-life-form, February 10, 2015

8. Shaw, Scott Richard, *Planet of Bugs,* University of Chicago Press, Chicago, 2014, p. 190

9. Jabr, Ferris, "How Did Insect Metamorphosis Evolve?" *Scientific American,* August 10, 2012

10. Ibid

11. "Why are Insects So Successful?" Invertebrate Paleontology Collection, Museum Victoria, www.museumvictoria.com.au, Melbourne, Australia, 2015

12. Honovich, Nancy; Murawski, Darlyne, *The Ultimate Bugopedia,* National Geographic, Washington, DC, 2013, p. 19

13. Ibid., p. 18

14. Wilson, E. O., *Social Conquest of Earth,* Liveright Publishing Corp., N.Y., 2011, p. 110

15. Angier, Natalie, "Guardian of the Soil," *New York Times,* February 3, 2015

16. Fleming, Nic,"Which Life Form Dominates Earth?" www.bbc.com/earth/story/20150211-whats-the-most-dominant-life-form, February 10, 2015

17. Wilson-Rich, Noah, *The Bee,* Princeton University Press, Princeton, N.J., 2014, p. 96

18. Shaw, Scott Richard, *Planet of Bugs,* University of Chicago Press, Chicago, 2014, p. 18

19. Ibid, p. 19

20. McKibben, Bill, *Eaarth,* St. Martin's Griffin, N.Y., 2011, p. 1

21. Sacks, Jeffrey, *The Age of Sustainable Development,* Columbia University Press, N.Y., 2015, p. 75

22. Ibid, p. 78

23. Nye, Bill, *Unstoppable,* St. Martin's Press, N.Y., 2015, p. 44

24. Mooney, Chris, "The World's Wide Web," *The Washington Post,* February 16, 2016

25. McKibben, Bill, *The End of Nature,* Random House, N.Y., 1989, 2006, p. 13

26. "A World On Fire," *The Economist,* February 27, 2016

27. Mooney, Chris, "The World's Wide Web," *The Washington Post,* February 16, 2016

28. "The Extinction Crisis," Center for Biological Diversity, www.biologicaldiversity.org/programs/biodiversity/elements_of_biodiversity/extinction_crisis, 2016

29. Paramaguru, Kharunya, "Rethinking Our Risky Reliance on Rare Earth Metals," *Time,* December 20, 2013

30. Klum, Mattias; Rockström, Johan, *Big World Small Planet,* Yale University Press, New Haven and London, 2015, p. 102

31. Ibid, p. 108

32. "Climate Change 2007: Synthesis Report," Intergovernmental Panel on Climate Change (IPCC), Geneva, Switzerland, 2008, p. 2

33. Nye, Bill, *Unstoppable,* St. Martin's Press, N.Y., 2015, p. 38

34. Anand, Guta, "As Air Worsens, New Dehli Takes to Masks," *New York Times,* March 2, 2016

35. Fears, Darryl, "More Than 5 Million People Will Die From a Frightening Cause: Breathing," *The Washington Post,* February 12, 2016

36. Wong, Edward, "Smog So Thick, Beijing Comes to a Standstill," *New York Times,* December 9, 2015

37. Kolbert, Elizabeth, "The Siege of Miami," *The New Yorker,* December 21-28, 2015

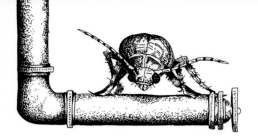

38 Nye, Bill, *Unstoppable,* St. Martin's Press, N.Y., 2015, p. 44

39 Romm, Joseph, *Climate Change,* Oxford University Press, N.Y., 2016, p. xv

40 Bloomberg, Michael; Paulson, Hank; Steyer, Tom, *Risky Business,* riskybusiness.org/site/assets/uploads/2015/09/RiskyBusiness_Report_WEB_09_08_14.pdf, June 2014

41 Kolbert, Elizabeth, "The Siege of Miami," *The New Yorker,* December 21-28, 2015

42 Burleigh, Nina, "Flood? What Flood?" *Newsweek,* February 5, 2016

43 Mooney, Chris, "Rising Sea Levels Threaten U.S. Cities," *The Washington Post,* October 13, 2015

44 Abel, David, "Climate Change Could Be Even Worse For Boston Than Previously Thought," *The Boston Globe,* June 22, 2016

45 Parker, Laura, "Treading Water," *National Geographic,* February 2015, p. 116

46 *The State of Food and Agriculture 2016,* Food and Agriculture Organization of the United Nations, Rome, www.fao.org/3/a-i6030e.pdf

47 "The ThirdPole Datanet," *Understanding Asia's Water Crisis,* thethirdpole.net, data.thethirdpole.net, 2016

48 "Unholy Woes, India's Water Nightmare," *The Economist,* May 14, 2016, p. 29

49 Wong, Edward, "Chinese Glacier's Retreat Signals Trouble for Asian Water Supply," *New York Times,* December 8, 2015

50 McKibben, Bill, *Eaarth,* St. Martin's Giffin, N.Y., 2011, p. 7

51 World Water Assessment Programme, *Water For a Sustainable World,* 2015, UNESCO, Paris

52 Romm, Joseph, *Climate Change,* Oxford University Press, N.Y., 2016, p. 123

53 Frankel, Todd, "The World's Aquifers Are Being Drained," *The Washington Post,* June 21, 2015

54 Romm, Joseph, *Climate Change,* Oxford University Press, N.Y., 2016, p. 125

55 Buckley, Chris; Piao, Venessa, "Rural Water, Not City Smog, May Be China's Pollution Nightmare," *New York Times,* April 12, 2016

56 Mann, Michael; Krump, Lee, *Dire Predictions,* 2nd Ed, Penguin Random House, N.Y., 2015. p. 34

57 Abel, David, "Scientist Call Last Month Warmest on Record," *The Boston Globe,* August 17, 2016

58 Cullen, Heidi, "Think Its Hot Now? Just Wait," *New York Times,* August 21, 2016

59 Mann, Michael; Kemp, Lee, *Dire Predictions,* 2nd Edition, Penguin Random House, N.Y., 2015, p. 100

60 Romm, Joseph, *Climate Change,* Oxford University Press, N.Y., 2016, p. 118

61 Kolbert, Elizabeth, *The Sixth Extinction,* Henry Holt and Co., N.Y., 2014, p. 120

62 Zimmer, Carl, "Ocean Life Faces Extinction," *New York Times,* January 16, 2015

63 "The Extinction Crisis," Center for Biological Diversity, www.biologicaldiversity.org/programs/biodiversity/elements_of_biodiversity/extinction_crisis, 2016

64 Zielinski, Sara, "Ocean Dead Zones Are Getting Worse," Smithsonian.com, www.smithsonianmag.com/science-nature/ocean-dead-zones-are-getting-worse-globally-due-climate-change-180953282/, November 10, 2014

65 Parker, Laura, "Eight Million Tons of Plastic Dumped in Ocean Every Year," *National Geographic,* February 13, 2015

66 Nvwer, Rachael, "The Blackmarket Trade for Endangered Animals Florishes on the Web," *Newsweek,* October 30, 2014

67 Mooney, Chris, "The World's Wide Web," *The Washington Post,* February 16, 2016

68 Bekoff, Marc, "The Exotic Pet Trade," *Huffington Post,* www.huffingtonpost.com/marc-bekoff/the-exotic-pet-trade-horr_1_b_9175608.html, February 9, 2016

69 "The Dirty Side of the Exotic Animal Trade," *Animal Issues Digest,* Born Free, USA, Vol. 34, No. 2, www.bornfreeusa.org/articles.php?more=1&p=180, June 15, 2003

70 Harvey, Chelsea, "Report Warns of Planet's Plunging Wildlife Populations," *The Washington Post,* Oct 30, 2016.

71 "Botany at Bay," *The Economist,* May 14, 2016, p. 71

72 Wilson, E. O., *Half Earth,* Liveright Publishing Corp., N.Y., 2016, p. 187

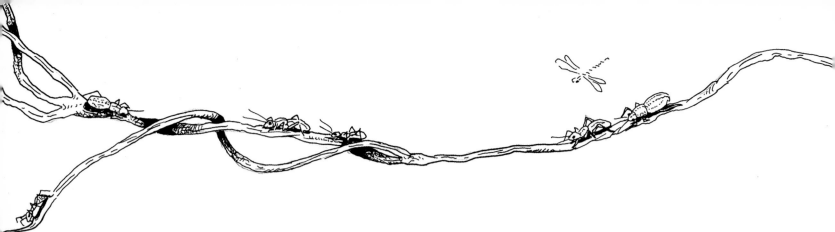

73 "The Extinction Crisis," Center for Biological Diversity, www.biologicaldiversity.org/programs/biodiveristy/elements_of_biodiversity/extinction_crisis, 2016

74 Schwartz, Steve, "Climate Change Countdown," *New York Times,* April 5, 2016

75 Ibid

76 "Pesticide Resistance," WGBH Foundation, www.pbs.org/wgbh/evolution/library, 1978

77 "Use of Insecticides," *Britannica,* www.britannica/technology/insecticides, 2016

78 Shaw, Scott Richard, *Planet of Bugs,* University of Chicago Press, Chicago, 2014, p. 5

79 Shayler, Hannah; McBride, Murray; Harrison, Ellen, "Sources and Impacts of Contaminants in Soils," Cornell Waste Management Institute, cwmi.css.cornell.edu/sourcesandimpacts.pdf, 2009

80 Glaser, Aviva, "Threatened Waters," *Pesticides and You,* Vol. 25, No. 4, 2005-06, p. 17

81 "Encephalization and Adaptability," Smithsonian's Human Origins Program, http://humanorigins.si.edu/research/climate-research/effects, 2016, p. 11

82 Klum, Mattias; Rockström, Johan, *Big World Small Planet,* Yale University Press, New Haven and London, 2015, p. 33

83 Mayer, Jane, *Dark Money,* Doubleday, N.Y., 2016, p. 202

84 Wilson, E. O., *The Social Conquest of Earth,* Liveright Publishing Corp., N.Y., 2011, p. 63

85 "Chemical Weapons," *Britannica,* www.britannica/technology/chemical-weapons, April 15, 2016

86 Brzezinski, Zbigniew, *Out of Control,* Simon and Schuster, N.Y., 1993, p.10, 17.

87 Sengupta, Somini, "Record 65 Million People Displaced," *New York Times,* June 20, 2016

88 Lorenz, Conrad, *On Aggression,* Houghton Mifflin Harcourt, Boston, 1966, p. 272

89 Fromm, Eric, *The Anatomy of Human Destructiveness,* Henry Holt and Co., N.Y., 1973, p. 223

90 Russell, Bertrand

91 Lorenz, Konrad, *On Aggression,* Houghton Mifflin Harcourt, Boston, 1966, p. 267

92 Fromm, Eric, *The Anatomy of Human Destructiveness,* Henry Hold and Co., N.Y., 1973, p. 230

93 Medalia, Jonathan, "Terrorist Nuclear Attach on Seaports: Threats and Responses," *Congressional Research Service (CRS) Report for Congress,* Jan. 24, 2005

94 Charlemagne, "Commented Out," *The Economist,* June 25, 2016

95 Brood, William; Sanger, David, "Race Escalates for Latest Class of Nuclear Arms," *New York Times,* April 17, 2016

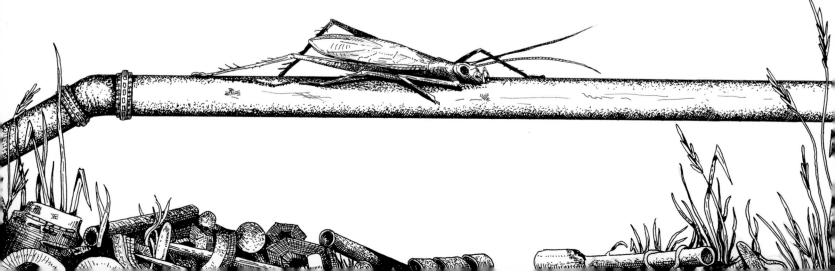

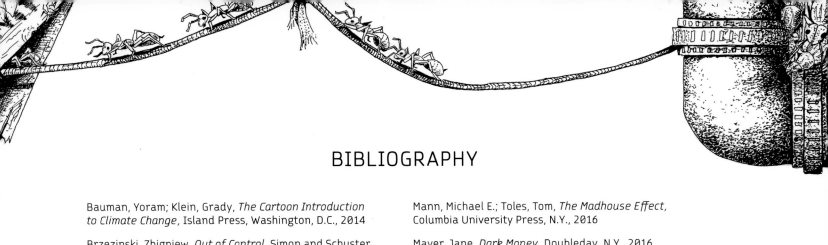

BIBLIOGRAPHY

Bauman, Yoram; Klein, Grady, *The Cartoon Introduction to Climate Change,* Island Press, Washington, D.C., 2014

Brzezinski, Zbigniew, *Out of Control,* Simon and Schuster, N.Y., 1993

Carson, Rachel, *Silent Spring,* Houghton Mifflin Harcourt, Boston, 1962

Climate Control, *Global Weirdness,* Vintage Books, N.Y., 2013

Elliot, Long; Hershberger, Wil, *The Songs of Insects,* Houghton Mifflin Company, Boston, 2006

Flannery, Tim, *The Weather Makers,* Grove Press, N.Y., 2005

Fromm, Eric, *The Anatomy of Human Destructiveness,* Henry Holt and Co., N.Y., 1973

Honovich, Nancy; Murawski, Darlyne, *The Ultimate Bugopedia,* National Geographic, Washington, DC, 2013

Janzon, Lars-Ake ; Hallman, John, *Bugs Up Close,* Skyhorse Publishing, N.Y., 2012

Klein, Naomi, *This Changes Everything,* Simon and Schuster, N.Y., 2014

Kolbert, Elizabeth, *The Sixth Extinction*, Henry Holt and Co., N.Y., 2014

Klum, Mattias; Rockström, Johan, *Big World Small Planet,* Yale University Press, New Haven and London, 2015

Kump, Lee R.; Mann, Michael E., *Dire Predictions*, Penguin Random House, N.Y., 2015

LeShan, Lawrence, *The Psychology of War,* Helios Press, N.Y., 1992

Lorenz, Konrad, *On Aggression,* Houghton Mifflin Harcourt, Boston, 1966

Mann, Michael E., *The Hockey Stick and the Climate Wars,* Columbia University Press, N.Y., 2012

Mann, Michael E.; Toles, Tom, *The Madhouse Effect,* Columbia University Press, N.Y., 2016

Mayer, Jane, *Dark Money,* Doubleday, N.Y., 2016

McKibben, Bill, *Eaarth,* St. Martin's Griffin, N.Y., 2011

McKibben, Bill, *The End of Nature,* Random House, N.Y., 1989, 2006

National Audubon Society, *Field Guide to North American Insects and Spiders,* Alfred A. Knoff, N.Y., 1980

Nye, Bill, *Unstoppable,* St. Martin's Press, N.Y., 2015

Paulson, Dennis, *Dragonflies and Damselflies of the West,* Princeton University Press, Princeton, 2009

Phillips, David M., *Art and Architecture of Insects,* University Press of New England, Lebanon, 2014

Romm, Joseph, *Climate Change,* Oxford University Press, N.Y., 2016

Sacks, Jeffrey D., *The Age of Sustainable Development,* Columbia University Press, N.Y., 2015

Sagan, Scott D; Waltz, Kenneth N., *The Spread of Nuclear Weapons,* W.W. Norton and Co., N.Y., 2013

Shaw, Scott Richard, *Planet of the Bugs,* University of Chicago Press, Chicago, 2014

Walters, Martin, *The Illustrated World Encyclopedia of Insects,* Lorenz Books, London, 2014

Wilson, Edward O., *Half-Earth,* Liveright Publishing Corp., N.Y., 2016

Wilson, Edward O., *The Social Conquest of Earth,* Liveright Publishing Corp., N.Y., 2011

Wilson-Rich, Noah, *The Bee,* Princeton University Press, Princeton, 2014

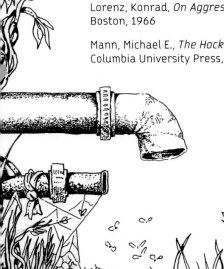

ACKNOWLEDGMENTS

This book is the result of meaningful contributions by many. The graphic design of the book was done by Lloyd Greenberg, LLC., specifically Vida Russell and Lloyd Greenberg. They made this book look better than I could have imagined. Greg Staley, an art documentation photographer, assured that many of my illustrations were beautifully transferred to print, as did Boston Photo Imaging, Boston, as well as Dodge Chrome, Washington, DC. The folks at Stanhope Framers, Somerville, Mass. also encouraged in a way they did not realize.

The idea to illustrate insects was driven by the sculptures, art shows, and encouragement of Joan Danziger. It was from thinking about and drawing insects that this story line grew.

The book, at its various stages, was read, commented on, and improved by Mel Scovell, Bob Friedman, Steve Sullivan, Steve Stevick, Nancy Raine, Mimi and Chas Wood, Betsy Seifter, Phil Balboni, Michael Butt, Ben Jacobs, Stuart Lemle and Steve Vetter.

But, above all others has been the love, support, insight, encouragement and guidance of my wife, Perrin Ireland. I could have easily faltered at many stages of this process, if not for Perrin. I love you.

Finally, my hope is that our grandson, Jackson, and our nephews and nieces, see a better world, because we regained our senses.

Berkeley, our dog, inspires me to believe that we can do better for creatures on this earth.